freedom's edge

*To Anthony Minghella.*

*Victoria Ginn*

# freedom's edge

## victoria ginn

HAZARD PRESS
publishers

*Author's Note*

The story *Freedom's Edge* is a re-construction of events based on the memory of my journey into Afghanistan in 1978. The names of some persons have been altered so as to avoid any misrepresentation.

This is a true story, the experiences and sequence of events happening as written.

Excerpts from the poems 'Beauty' and 'Cats', by Baudelaire, from the translations in *Selected Poems* by Joanna Richardson reprinted here with the permission of Curtis Brown on behalf of Joanna Richardson. Copyright © Joanna Richardson, 1975.

The poem 'Slave Boy' by Yusuf ibn Harūn al-Ramādi, from *Poems of Arab Andalusia*, translated from the Spanish version by Cola Franzen reprinted here by permission of City Lights Publishers. Copyright © Cola Franzen, 1989.

First published 2001
Copyright © 2001 Victoria Ginn

The author asserts her moral rights in the work

ISBN 1-877161-86-1

Published by Hazard Press Limited
P.O. Box 2151, Christchurch, New Zealand
Cover and page design by Working Ideas, Christchurch

Printed in New Zealand by Printlink

# Acknowledgments

The author extends her deep gratitude to the following people and organisations:

Sherril Catsburg, Berys Harries, Joanne MacKay, Selina Roebeck and all those responsible for the typing and photocopying of *Freedom's Edge* during its many revisions.

Robert Ian Axford for his printing of the photographic plates.

Mary Doby, who was the first to point out the need for slimmer sentences, Steff Birch, who continued the process, Selah Weingott, for her acute understanding of the written language, Diane Kearns, Bridget Wilson, Rachel Scott, Antoinette Wilson, Lesley Beaven for further contributing to the editorial process.

Lee Jensen, Richard Ollivier and Graphic Solutions.

My publishers, Hazard Press Ltd, for their patience and standard of excellence in every aspect of the production of this book.

Those various friends, family, acquaintances and strangers for their support and interest, with an extra thanks to Tony Hiles, Martin P. Connell, Peter Barker, Pamela Fleming, Natasha Baskerville-Robinson. Taly Rudy-Hoekman for the midnight coffees and conversation, Claudia Carr-Levy, Anna Campion, Nan Berkeley, Vivian Lynn, Robert Franken, Raouf and Evelyne Siegrist and the pianist Philippa Ward.

This project has been assisted by the Commonwealth Government through the Australia Council's arts funding and advisory board.

*Freedom's Edge* is dedicated to those persons who assisted in my release from Afghanistan in 1978, among whom are my late parents Ellinore and Russell Ginn. To these people I owe my life, and irrepressible love of life.

*Front cover image:* Night Market, Peshawar, Pakistan

# Introduction

In 1978 Victoria Ginn travelled to Afghanistan to photograph wild places and the people who lived there.

Boys in the photographs she took are today's commanders in the religiously fired Taleban militia, whose white flag flutters over two-thirds of this destroyed country. For their mothers and sisters, life has returned to Year Zero.

The Taleban fighters grew up in filthy, dirt-poor camps in Pakistan and Iran, home to five million refugees during ten years of Russian occupation from 1979.

Their mothers and sisters stayed in the tents while the men plotted to overthrow the oppressors across the border.

Back in their homeland today, as in the refugee camps, women in Afghanistan are confined, denied education and forbidden to linger in public or talk to foreigners. In the capital of Kabul windows have been painted out or replaced with opaque glass as the sight of women's faces is believed to corrupt men. Outside their homes, women must wear a burka to cover them from head to toe, a narrow gauze panel provided for their eyes.

In a harsh version of the sharia, the ancient Muslim legal code, adulterers are stoned to death in a religious ceremony not allowed to be witnessed by non-believers, and the hands and feet of thieves are routinely amputated.

Under picturesque mulberry bushes and blossoming almond trees the Office for the Propagation of Virtue and the Prohibition of Vice smashes television sets, video recorders, stereo systems and cameras.

Deprived of education, except for years of obsessively studying the Koran, and of all entertainment, the Taleban are re-creating the only life they've known, one of illiterate brutality born in the refugee camps.

Victoria Ginn's story is not about the nuts and bolts of the beginnings of the Afghan war, though it does paint a background of the political machinations and underlying sense of the time.

It is the subjective story of an unsuspecting white 'Christian' interloper, a traveller and seeker of truth, confused by and caught up in the maelstrom of an overwhelmingly alien culture.

It is also about an ingenuous young woman whose desire to connect with the world through her camera lens is an almost irresistible compulsion until, as the result of a hashish smuggling charge, she forfeits her freedom.

Ultimately the drugs, her incarceration in a Muslim jail, the manipulations of a sexually molesting high government minister and the revolution are vehicles to a different end as the author makes an internal journey.

Externally, it is a journey whose dramatic rhythms fold into one another with an undercurrent of sensuality. This is a true story about a 24-year-old New Zealand woman whose actions and mystical, spiritual nature cause her to confront complicated forces in a nation, its people and its landscape.

*Selah Weingott*
*London, May 1997*

A promise honoured.

# part one

*…there is no great difference between the memory of a dream
and the memory of a reality…*
Marcel Proust

## ONE

# 1978

I am way up here looking way down there, at the vast, shivering blue South Pacific ocean, in a straight-winged metal bird tirelessly aloft in a horizon-green and empty sky… Infinite space…

Abstract shapes – splashes of clouds – puffy-white baby clouds sitting as black-white polka dots upon the blue. Below, a cloud desert composed of soft, grey-white hillocks and footprint-neverness… a silent harmony.

Light changing: a heavenly gold, pink; purple cloud-mountains, rising, transforming into giant grey-blue faces-forms – a foal, a monster, a mare. Fading into night.

We are descending, into the blinking night-colours of Hong Kong.

Refuelled, we fly back up into Asia's high night darkness.

Darkness.

Descending now… toward a sprawling but more humble sea of lights – patterns of light upon the night. Delhi. *India.*

I have never been to India and know virtually nothing about it. Even less about my further destinations, Pakistan and Afghanistan.

Anticipation nervousness excitement. The plane touches down – screaming roar – catapults me into hot sounds, night-chilled, strange-tongued. Burning eyes…

Culture shock. I'm an alien! My feet are on an altogether different ground.

Jet-lagged. Sleepless.

I taxi into the night…

Where do I come from? Some might say idealism, and foolhardiness. I am of an artistic sensibility.

As to what I do: I am absorbed in the art of 'reflection', of mirrors and lenses – photography. My aim is to document the human psyche via the human face – exposer of emotion, symbol, *archetype*. Inner-outer shadow-light.

The camera is my third eye; my naivety the key to my 'seeing'.

But there's another, more personal reason for this journey. I am a geographically remote islander – a rebellious fourth-generation 'new world' descendant of British colonisation of the South Pacific. A child of storming seas, wild winds, cliff-edge isolation, I yearn to know and belong to the wider world. Merge with the mass. Try to 'see'.

But it's a fog – I'm fogged, misted in culture shock. It's an electric animal alertness mixed with a feeling of having slept badly; reality is pin-sharp yet dreamlike.

I am, alone, in an Enormous Foreign City.

I tell my diary:

> *A jolt of fear within… a wild, heart-beating million-automobiled lawlessness beep-beeping, smoke choking their way around nonchalantly sacred cows… Walking, leprous hands beggar stretch as surly-eyed and dirt-ragged thieves shift in and out of this traffic of flesh… following, as the sun touches my back, as the cold Himalayan wind blows dust and a thousand smells; shifting; whispers loudly bounce within the white dome-womb of the Taj Mahal. A child cries beneath my window. A girl defecates on the brown grass; looks behind, moves on.*

I have a contact – someone I don't know but whom I can visit. She is an artist, a portraitist living in the back streets of a thin-bodied people-thick Old Delhi.

A taxi delivers me to her address.

A tap on her door. It opens onto quick-darting eyes and a kindly face – that of a diminutive Indian woman. She ushers me into a musty room, wherein an ailing and elderly European woman invites me to sit in an empty chair, close to her.

She herself sits in a rickety chair, a grey blanket over her knees, an old, deep-purple hand-knitted cardigan hung loose over her thin wrists. Her head and bone-thin, deeply wrinkled face are bowed, bent toward her chest. A few crusts of toast remain on a plate close to her.

The room is large, the only light the morning sun filtering through cracks in the shutters at the far end of the room, a light too weak to warm the wintry chill or provide anything more than a shadowy illumination.

Scattered all around the room are painted portraits – her paintings.

The artist had been a friend of Nehru's, who had sat for her, she tells me. But she can no longer paint. Arthritis. I sneak another peek at her hands. They look like gnarled claws.

I look again at her unframed paintings, at the eyes and identities of her subjects; they're fading as decay quietly devours them.

The Indian woman is bringing in a tray. 'Tea?' the artist asks, bending her head and looking at me with old blue eyes.

The hot glass warms my cold fingers as I sit and sip.

Rats. There are rats squeaking and scuffling and leaping along a ledge midway up the dusty walls.

The room, this woman: there is something sad and forgotten about them. Impoverishment and loneliness. Is this the fate of the artist, a Kali-esque cannibalism of creativity by poverty and isolation? Well, *not* for me. Of this I am *determined*.

The artist, rising, follows me stiffly to her door. Not into the bright daylight, but into sufficient light for me to realise how ill she is. Her eyes are turning upward, are disappearing behind her eyelids. I am looking at a grey-white blank, a sightless void. 'There is danger ahead of you,' she whisper-murmurs. She's dying before my eyes.

I hear her message. Danger. Slowly a small hand reaches out and takes hers, draws her inside. But… I'm twenty-three 'immortal' years of age.

*Diary:*
*Awandering, awandering wild and free, no solid walls imprison me.*

One week in Delhi has passed: clicking and tripping my blink-blank way through her crowded streets, temples, marketplaces, gawping at her ripped-mouthed, bloodied, fingerless but sharp-eyed humanity; gasping at her fire-food, resisting the entreaties of her street hawkers trying to con me into buying a host of useless goods. Acclimatising.

I'm now ready to move north.

# two

The train steam-puffs its massive hulk to a halt. Amritsar railway station, from my carriage window, is seething with wild-haired Sikhs yelling and running along the platform. A band of unturbaned holy warriors, their black eyes glint fanatically, as if in compensation for the dull-brown of the rusty swords they brandish aloft the crowd.

Sikhism is a religion that preaches universal tolerance.

Dismounting, I dodge my way between pin-thin, naked-legged Indian porters bent beneath huge square sacks, to the international boundary line. And the India-Pakistan border police.

I'm a blonde (disoriented rather than dizzy) blue-eyed young woman dressed in warm, body-hugging clothes. An individualist.

The police smile, linger, finger every shape, protrusion and fold of my luggage – my clothes, that is. They don't look anywhere else. Except at my face. It's personable, in flesh and passport.

They stamp my passport. A sense of satisfaction fills me – my first border crossed.

Now heading for Lahore. Pakistan.

Lahore railway station. Something's *different*. In my brief time in Delhi I had perceived a sort of 'Siva-Sakti' tolerance, an old and dusty gentleness. Here there is a sharpness. A racial difference? Sharp-nosed, unsmiling staring. It's disconcerting, so much so that it prompts me to buy a ticket out, onwards, to Peshawar, in the north of Pakistan.

The train is due to leave in – I glance at my wristwatch – eight hours. Enough time to explore and photograph Lahore.

No one, not one of the glum dummies, shifts from its staring stance and offers to assist me with my luggage – my camera case, film case, suitcase. And they are heavy. Thankfully I am strong enough to lug these beloved encumbrances outside the terminal.

The harsh light of late winter flashes on the window of a swooping taxi. A taxi. Now to find a hotel.

Here, as in Delhi, the traffic moves according to the law of chaos: a double lane with vehicles jammed five-ten abreast, all – their drivers bewitched with craziness – beeping-honking, fighting to move in the same direction. A similar 'double' lane is zigzagging, stalling, jamming, motor-screaming in what ought to be the opposite direction.

Fortunately there is a dividing line between the two lanes: a narrow strip of raised concrete that appears, to my driven gaze, to be home to the outcasts and the dying. Like pieces of discarded and rumpled paper they are spread along it, their indrawn and unmoving forms oblivious to the impatient sounds and clouds of spent diesel belching from the traffic.

Except for one whose image grabs me. Cross-legged, bolt upright, face raised, his wide-open eyes, which seem weirdly to encompass mine, fixed on the invisible. I flash past.

The taxi driver deposits me at the entrance to a hotel not far from the railway station. I find and speak to the manager, who permits me to store my baggage for a few hours.

I'm here, in Lahore, Pakistan, I tell myself.

Now, with one of my cameras – my Hasselblad – it's into the streets… and the communal openness of Asia's pavement shops. Side streets, away from the fumes and noise, the areas where the people are: tinkers, tobacco sellers, silversmiths, potmakers, barbers…

*Click*… a man standing three-quarters to me, pointing his index finger at the shadow of another.

…a street barber and client and a small third head peeping around the client's head. Strong lights, strong shadows.

…a tobacco merchant, a spice seller, sitting amid boxes of coloured spices.

…a shoeshine lad with blackened hands and a grimy face, looking incredulous.

…a tea maker, three blue teapots one on top of the other in front of him. A thin pipe between his fingers.

…a cobbler hammering cut and glued leather. He stops his work, stares at me.

…another cobbler. Behind him, stacks of hides await their turn to walk again.

…a fruiterer – his face looks out from behind his trays of produce. Looks at me.

…a group of men staring at me – old men, young men (apron shirts, baggy pants, subdued greens, blues, mauves, grey) all agog… staring men.

I lift my face and look ahead: male faces crane out from every corner, every shopfront, all the way down this small street.

*Staring* at me.

Where are the women?

It's too unnerving. I look for a way out – a small alley – disappear into it. Old broken-brick walls block out the harsh sunlight. It's quiet.

I glance behind to see if I'm followed. No. I slow down. There's peace in the shadows. Cool, calming.

I explore the shade. It is deepening. Deepening into, over there, a pile of coal: two eyes, looking at me. A woman! I step toward her. Her age is indeterminate.

I move closer, bowing my head to the viewer of my waist-held Hasselblad. She looks at my crown, unaware that I am studying her. The cold sheen of silver glistens from a dozen bracelets on each of her wrists. On her naked shoulder a large raised scar also glistens, faintly. Her deep brown-black skin has almost merged with the black coal dust and surrounding shadow; only the line of her sitting form separates her from total darkness.

Her meagre possessions are displayed like precious things: a piece of wrapped cloth, three keys, a small silver chain, various coins, and two tattered banknotes – these are placed in a semicircle on her black coal-dust mound, and close to a soft-ragged fall of dusty-black cloth, her sari.

She's now staring at my camera lens – our eyes meet through the mirror.

I connect with her, photographically, impersonally. Yet not so impersonally that I don't feel. Her eyes, sad-soft… *Click*.

Now on through the alleyway, into sunlight and a different street.

Walking.

'Shish. Shish.' A voice – question? It's coming from that group of young men standing indolently around their scooter cabs; they're huskily – 'Shish? Shish?' – calling to me.

What is it? There's an eagerness. They want me to come over. One is waving something in his hand, beckoning to me.

They look inoffensive, smiling.

It is a cigarette with a screwed tip, being waved excitedly at me. 'Shish shish.' Why is this twisted cigarette causing such smiling excitement?

They want me to smoke it? Is it what I think?

They look harmless…The allure of the exotic draws me in.

Into the back seat of a two-seater scooter cab, which somehow manages to accommodate three four five thin, brown, highly enthusiastic youths. Elbows and eyes.

Lighting, eagerly sucking… a whiff, a rich, intensely pleasurable scent filters into my nostrils. It is *hashish*! – *the* drug of my 'liberated' generation.

Inhaling, eagerly, deeply. Just what I've been secretly, delinquently wishing for. Coughing violently.

The atmosphere's *changing*. The youths' faces sinister, their red-veined eyes bulging. Claustrophobia overwhelms me. Got to get out.

But as I lurch out of the cab they follow, encircle me: ten, twenty – forty, fifty, a hundred… a mob. All men – many-headed: *closing in.*

I'm trembling inwardly. I'm very stoned. What to do?

*Camera*. I unsling it from my shoulder and aim it at the feverish mob. The view through the lens is a square border in black, the left is to the right.

A surge of relief: they're falling back. Are smiling. Posing.

I seize the opportunity: gesture dramatically, bow my head, look into the camera viewer, they can't see my eyes this way. And bending-bowing like this gives the impression that I am praying.

I fiddle with the aperture and the distance knobs, telling myself to *keep pointing* the camera at them, all the while shouting directions, coercing the mob to… they're retreating.

Openings, gaps appear in this phalanx of bodies. Can I get through, that gap?

But, what is *that*, behind the body of men? Horror. It's skeletal. An old woman!

She's slumped against those grey stone steps – she's on the sixth one. Soft folds of cloth are rotting into her, giving an illusory suppleness to her decaying body. The skin on her face is a tight brown mask.

A cadaver. And no one has bothered to bury it.

Total, blood-freezing terror: her eyes, her *dead* eyes… *staring* into mine.

Something, someone taps my shoulder. A peasant boy. He has sensed my fear. I fix on his hand, on the direction of his extended fingers. Up, up, up the steps. To where? There, a white mosque, and inside, the backs of rows of yellow-robed men, bowed in prayer. Sublime: yellow, white. *Peace*. My fear subsides.

I turn back to photograph the spectre, to capture her with my camera's one black eye. I hold my breath for steadiness and face her, a *nightmare*, death face. *Click*.

But why this feeling that I must transform the photographic negative into its print positive as quickly as possible? The knowing is inexplicable.

The crowd of men are freeze-framed, still haven't moved or spoken. Did they too feel what I felt when that cadaver's eyes locked into mine?

*A chance.*

I have broken free. Moving quickly.

A trickle of them follow me into a busy street – traffic and pedestrians.

A youth walking along the pavement toward me catches my eye. He is dressed in neat, Western clothes. He's approaching. Bows before me. 'Can I be of any service to madam?' *My language* – he speaks English!

I glance sideways at the stragglers who have now caught up. He shoos them away. He obviously has some authority.

'I am a student at Lahore University, and I must tell you, madam, that Islamic law does not permit women onto the streets unless they are wearing a burka, a garment covering the body from head to foot. There are exceptions but only in the more modern areas. In the place you have been, only whores and beggars go without the burka.'

I feel put upon. What this student is telling me has nothing to do with *me*. 'Where I come from women can wear what they like, and walk anywhere,' I tell him haughtily.

'You need a guide, madam,' he replies. 'It is too dangerous here for you to walk alone. My name is Hammid and I would be greatly honoured if you will permit me to be your guide during your visit to my city.'


## three


Hammid asks if I would like to have a look at some of the older areas of Lahore, and meet his family. He's fresh-looking, clean, middle-class educated. He leads me toward a stationary vehicle.

We hire and climb into it. It is a three-wheel, diesel-puffing, whining two-seater scooter cab.

Now we are manoeuvring through the residential backstreets. Puttering and beeping, rattling and snaking between mud-brick houses. Through intersecting alleyways. Passing pastel-draped bodies, still and moving.

Back and back, reaching into what looks like a biblical time.

A burst of colour – fruit on a fruit stall.

Hammid leans forward, speaks to the cabby. We stop outside one of an infinity of terracotta houses.

Extracting a large silver key from his trouser pocket, Hammid unlocks the front door and ushers me in. I follow him through a narrow hallway into a room filled with disembodied faces staring stiffly from stand-up frames, presumably family portraits. Below these, close together on a low divan, are two wide-eyed girls in their late teens, staring incredulously at me. Hammid's sisters.

Fluster and fluffle, amidst which Hammid excuses himself, telling me he will return in one hour.

The sisters sit close together on the divan; I sit on a low cushioned stool. Between us is a small rectangular table on which a plate of liquid-looking cakes and three glasses of tea have appeared. Goody, afternoon tea. But where's the milk?

Effusive smiles and gesticulations. 'Beautiful!' they utter in unison.

I am still very stoned. The cardamom-flavoured black tea is furry on my tongue.

The cakes, the sisters want me to eat these sugary pastries.

Politely nodding. 'No thank you.'

'Beautiful! Beautiful!' Beautiful seems to be the only word they know.

'*You* are beautiful,' I say back to them – their innocent wide black eyes.

Time passes to a musical accompaniment of soft cooing 'beautifuls'.

Then Hammid returns. I'm to say goodbye to the sisters.

Outside, Hammid turns his silver key and locks his beautiful sisters in.

Two lookalike young men are waiting in the scooter cab. Four of us are in the two-person back seat of a rattling scooter cab. *Squashed.*

We stop and climb into a large van. For more comfortable sightseeing I presume. Zigzagging across the city, stopping here, there, to pick up Hammid's friends. The van fills with Hammid's friends. He's showing me off.

They are all very polite and shy. All students, studying engineering, politics, philosophy, international relations, they tell me.

They are all reverent, until one of them asks: 'You are a movie star?' his voice rising on the 'star'.

An immediate change in the atmosphere; a disturbing eagerness. A body shifts behind me, pushes forward. A face bends around my neck.

'Please, madam, just one kiss, to remember for all my life,' bursts the youth sitting next to me, gazing imploringly at me. I laugh and think how sweet it is of him to *beg,* to long so for a kiss. Everyone laughs.

'Please, madam, just one kiss.' He is in earnest.

'No,' I say with firmness.

'*Please*, madam.' He's not listening to me.

The dozen youths sitting in the back are all now calling, pleading, breathing down my neck: 'Please, madam, just one *kisssss.*'

Distance, keep your distance, I tell them with my eyes.

'Take me back to where you met me, please, Hammid.' No reply. He's deliberately not hearing me.

It is mid-evening. After at least three circuits of the city and five hours of relentless 'one kiss' requests I have finally convinced my captors to let me go.

Hammid draws up within a hundred feet of the hotel.

Leaping out of the van, I make a beeline for the door. I'm thirsty and fatigued. 'Where's the restaurant?'

There… and over there a single empty table in a corner.

At last; hidden from unwanted attention.

The room is busy, filled with black-haired men who, from sitting in lone, grey-suited indifference to one another, are shifting their chairs and simultaneously their gaze in order to better see, or be seen by, me.

They're scrutinising me! Is there no space I can call my own here?

A cheap white china cup two-thirds filled with an equally white, lukewarm liquid. Tea. *Drink.* Drunk.

Eight hours in Lahore are up.

I return to the station the same way as I came: my signpost, revealed by the headlights of the passing traffic, is the form and waxen face of the dying man I had passed earlier in the day. He is still immobilised, waiting, staring toward the invisible.

The station. My camera case strap across my left shoulder, my film case strap on the opposite shoulder, and my suitcase in my hand, I bustle toward the ladies' carriage in the first-class section and climb aboard.

The carriage is warm and occupied by a sprawl of Pakistani women chatting animatedly to one another, their bodies wrapped in gorgeous woollen shawls, their faces and heads uncovered.

I pass between a weave of colour and scented air to my seat.

The train slurs away, its massive body grinding, creaking, groaning as it slowly gains momentum. In a stupor I study the plump, olive-skinned faces of the women, their full-lipped clean-eyed ease, the generous folds of cloth wrapping their relaxed bodies. So secure, so safely innocent somehow.

How different from the predatory men in Lahore. They are so definitely, *separately,* women. Where is the happy balance, the meeting point between male and female? Is it in the sexless bodies of the dying? I'm too tired suddenly to pursue this. Cushioning my head between my seat and the train's window, I drift off into a sitting sleep.

four

The train is galloping when I open my eyes. Chh-chh-chh-ch… Its iron muscles churning. Outside, on the outer pane of glass, a blur of rain rivulets streak across the window, diffusing and texturising the low blue light of dawn yawning across the 'rushing' wintry, grey-white landscapes beyond.

It's painterly; frozen.

Am I being watched? I can feel someone watching me… I turn and meet a pair of intelligent black-brown eyes belonging to the woman in the seat facing mine. She is wrapped in an abundance of rich red cloth. Long black hair. Pale olive skin.

Smiling at me, a warm and curious smile. She is gently edging me into wakefulness, conversation, speaking to me in English. Introducing herself: Saeeda. Telling me, with great pride, that her mother was Pakistan's first woman doctor.

Saeeda's destination, the village of Nowshera, draws near. 'Would you please come and stay at my house?' I am delighted. How unexpected and wonderful.

Nowshera is a quaint little station in the middle of nowhere. A *cold*, quaint little station.

A picturesque horse and carriage is waiting for her – us. Bells and coloured ribbons adorn the horse's tail and mane, a thick patchwork coloured blanket its body.

Climbing into the carriage, we quickly wrap ourselves in heavy woollen blankets. The ground is ice white.

Tinkling, tinkling our way through small cobblestone streets to the clip-clop of the horse's hoofs echoing off the roughly hewn stone walls of old houses. The village is asleep, silent but for our passage… to the first finger of the morning sun and a gathering of servants. The servants stand in line, awaiting their mistress.

Alighting, she steps graciously toward them. Smiles, embraces and hugs each one with a warmth normally bestowed on cherished blood relations. It is disarming, touching.

Laughter and happy chatter surrounds me, amidst which a tall, gentle-mannered man uplifts my luggage. Tucking it under his long arms, he leads me, with Saeeda, into the house. To my bedroom. It is big, and beautifully plain.

Introductions to the household follow. It is as large and as diverse as this villa appears to be: children, the husband, his mother, cousins, brothers, servants. I'm flattered by their warm and welcoming attentions.

Morning tea is served: small sweet balls of rice to fill my empty stomach, mashed date and almond cakes, endless glasses of pale green tea.

The villa is a rambling elegance of marble, stone, stucco, oiled timber, and leads out to stone courtyards, small waterfalls, budding trees and a spaciousness encased by high white walls. Hidden within a world, within a world.

I am blessed to be here.

Early evening; dinner time, and togetherness. I join the other members of the household, all sitting in a circle around large bowls of steaming white rice, spiced chicken, chopped coriander, red onions, mashed chickpeas, garlic crushed with chilli and oil, lamb kebabs, cucumber with yogurt. And great mounds of soft, freshly baked unleavened bread. All of which is placed on a large square of white cloth spread out on the floor. There are no forks, no knives, no spoons, no plates.

Our right hands reach out, finger-spoon the rice, dip the bread into the bowls of mashed food, finger-pick the kebabs and spiced chicken… All in a dignified and, but for the pleasure of eating, silent communalism.

This feast is followed by slices of fresh, cool, sweet tangy fruit. Then little bowls of lemon-scented water. For washing *the* hand.

A sudden arising, everyone is getting up. Is there to be no after-dinner conversation? They're all going into another room. Someone turns on a television set.

Out of politeness I join the household. A serious-looking political broadcaster appears and the volume turned to full. A deafening rant deals out – the news? What he's saying is as incomprehensible to me as the household's mesmerism. I withdraw.

Climb into a *cosy, clean, warm, heavenly* bed.

A soft knock on my bedroom door. It's Saeeda, coming to say goodnight. She sits on my bed, holds my hand, gazes down at me. A lovely, motherly warmth in her eyes, her hand. She's as pleased to have me as I am to be here.

Patterns of light stretch across the polished blue, brown, black marble hallway. The villa is quiet but feels warm, as if the household has been up and occupied for hours already.

Eyes of sunlight peer through a geometry of arches.

Saeeda's not here, her husband's not here, nor are her children. The servants are. They have been waiting for me to rise to give me breakfast: fruit, yogurt, bread and boiled eggs.

I'm free to take the day at my leisure, to acquaint myself with my surrounds, I assume. How civilised.

I venture out, walking in the opposite direction to the way Saeeda and I arrived, down a small broken road. Within a quarter of a mile the road splinters into rough tracks: a choice of paths. Which, where? The most trodden path.

It leads down to the crest of a small hill, overlooking what looks like a huge and strangely active 'rubbish dump': bits of tin, walls of cardboard, tattered canvas canopies, hillocks of debris – and *thousands* of people. A refugee camp? It must be. There is something so *unnatural* about this – why can't they spread out? It's unsettling. Where do they come from? Belong?

The splintered paths must be their tracks.

A glimpse is enough.

## five

My second day at Saeeda's and I'm to be entertained; Saeeda and her husband have organised for me to go on a sightseeing tour, alone with their chauffeur.

What a luxury, sitting in the black back seat of a comfortable modern car, with 'my chauffeur', an expanse of rolling hills and fields on either side.

We're heading toward Saeeda's husband's workplace. He is the chief engineer on a bridge-building project and I'm going to inspect his genius.

He leads me over to the site: hundreds of dainty-ankled donkeys are roped together in lines, hauling massive concrete girders across the ground. Others, to the thrash of whips and brays, are rope-levering them up and into position through an unfathomable system of pulleys. Up, and above an angry storm of wild water which, Saeeda's husband modestly boasts, 'neither Queen Victoria's nor Alexander the Great's armies could carve a way across'. He is the first to have devised a system of construction over the river.

His bridge-to-be is most impressive; a feat of engineering brilliance.

I photograph the donkeys, the ropes, the girders, the river, Saeeda's husband – a handsome man in his mid-forties.

The following day Saeeda's husband is on holiday. Friday is the Islamic day of rest, he tells me.

Would I like to go for a walk? The morning is crisp, bright – steaming breath in the shade, warm face in the sun. And I know he enjoys the opportunity to chat in English with me.

We are halfway across a large green field before I realise that we are walking on young *marijuana* plants, stretching as far as the eye can see. I'm incredulous. But should I pretend not to know? 'Is this marijuana we are walking on?' I ask tentatively, innocently.

Saeeda's husband bends down and casually pulls out a fistful of plants. 'Grows everywhere.' I have to ask him. 'What is the law here regarding marijuana, and hashish?' Tossing the wilting weed away, he replies with a folk story.

Once upon a time there lived a king who, though young and handsome, grew very bored with life. Nothing seemed able to stir him from his unhappiness – not women, not music, not possessions. Such was his anguish that a servant took courage and suggested he could help the king.

'I know a drug that will give you wondrous dreams and return your failing spirit to the beauty of life,' he said. The king ordered him to find this drug and upon taking it he indeed felt all the wonderful sensations the servant had predicted. He was so pleased that he called for his servant.

'This drug is so beautiful it must cost a great deal,' he exclaimed and offered his servant large lumps of gold to buy him more. 'Oh no, sir,' said the servant, 'this drug is so common that it costs not a thing.' The king then dismissed his servant, saying, 'If this drug is worthless it cannot be fit for a king.'

So, Saeeda's husband explains, hashish is regarded as the peasants' drug and in this sense remains outside political law. But it is illegal to take it out of the country.

Peasant or king, illusion or delusion, the story somehow opens for Saeeda's husband the door to an inner pain. He stops walking, and in a voice both confused and injured suddenly blurts: 'I love my wife but I no longer desire her. She is too fat and no longer feels like a woman to me.' He turns toward me. Continues: 'I am very puzzled that love for a woman can be free of desire.'

In a sense I am flattered to be confided in, to meet such openness. But then what am I hearing? Why is he betraying his intelligent, warm, lovely wife to me in this way?

Uncomfortable, I slowly swing around to walk back to the villa. I change the subject. 'In Lahore I noticed men walking hand in hand, and who were openly affectionate to each other. Is homosexuality common in your country?'

Saeeda's husband, accepting my non-reply, waxes philosophical: 'It is an ancient tradition of these areas of the world that men love boys and other men. It is a way of teaching young boys about the higher, more spiritual realms of love, as become men. It is friendship, *platonic* love. But sometimes a man cannot afford to have a wife.' He's looking at me in a slightly superior way. Covering himself?

The villa is in sight. I must take a last peek behind me, at our weaving path of crushed baby marijuana plants.

'Of course love for a woman can be free of desire,' I put in as we near the open door, with a smile.

The refugees are on my mind; I should visit the camp and photograph them. But I also know that they have already been utterly stripped of their sense of belonging and their privacy. It would be too much of an invasion for me to point my camera at them.

Instead I decide to visit the little cobblestone village Saeeda and I passed through on our way to her house.

It is as mysteriously silent during the day as it had been at dawn.

Focusing in; photographing in black and white – the relationship of lines. The lines cracking like old mud into a face, the strands of his white beard, his stained turban. The bricks and timber behind him. I press the shutter…

He remains unmoving, speechless, staring. I walk on.

Another old man, walking. A single strand of his white curl of beard waves out from his cheek into a block of line to the right of his forehead, a V of wings flying across his brow. Beneath a rope-twist cloud of cloth entwining his head, a landscape of ridges, valleys and cliffs cloth-spread about his shoulders. His eyes are hooded by a river-washed brush of eyebrow. Like those of a fox or a wizard.

I stop him in his tracks. He stares…

It is late afternoon, *cold*.

I return 'home' amid a pale snow-blue high-altitude light.

## six

A surprise: new guests have arrived. No less than, so I am told, the Afghanistan government's Minister of Police and his family. Civilised and gracious introductions and exchanges.

Mid-morning and our party takes a stroll around the garden, my hosts and their new guests talking effusively as we wander. As I can't understand the language I observe the signs of spring – the tiny pink tongues of almond blossoms breaking from their buds; the babbling of a small mountain stream frothing along a rock-manicured causeway. The little stream is fascinating with its miniature gradating waterfalls; bubbles of white within black cascades. It is so deliciously fresh-looking, *determined*.

Someone is behind me…

The government Minister from Afghanistan.

He's not interested in the waterfall. He wants to know where I come from. What my country is like. Sea foam, blue skies, summer and daydreams float innocently across my mind. 'Very green, mountainous, and surrounded by an enormous ocean,' I tell him.

'Very far away,' he rejoins, and tells me he has never seen an ocean, or been by the sea. His English is quite good, and he's pleasant enough. We polite-speak as we meander back to the group.

In the afternoon a treat: the Minister's three-year-old daughter is to dance for us, transforming herself into a superbly graceful glittering little butterfly, her little rainbow-slippered feet toe-drumming, her silken outstretched arms and tiny painted fingers weaving exquisite signs, her quick kohl-rimmed eyes sparkling like diamonds, little lipstick-red mouth smiling seductively…

The Minister stands alongside me as I watch his daughter dance. The mother stands opposite us and I can see she is ill at ease. She must be in her late thirties, though she looks older, disappointed.

As I glance at her she looks my way, fires me a disdainful stare. She is manicured, controlled. Middle-class and humourless, I decide.

It is early evening. There's an odd quiet within the villa. Something is up.

A gong sounds for supper. Not the usual knock on the door, a servant opening it and graciously telling me to 'come'.

The atmosphere in the dining circle is *too* formal, and judging by the household's unanimously lowered eyes this has to do with me.

Sensing my exclusion I withdraw as soon as the meal is over. I do not understand.

Saeeda's husband comes into my room in the early morning. He's sitting on my bed, looking troubled. He tells me that my presence is disturbing the Minister's wife. 'She has a jealous temperament. It will be better if you stay in a hotel in Peshawar.'

Confusion and sadness are my unspoken reply.

Saeeda doesn't come to say goodbye. Is she ashamed?

## SEVEN

A large and dirty-white hotel in a busy traffic zone in the city of Peshawar is my new abode. It is grubby and has an atmosphere like the concrete it is made of. But fortunately I am not to be completely abandoned. Saeeda's husband, in arranging this hotel room, has also arranged for one of her nephews to act as my guide and escort while I remain in the city.

He is Ahmed, a safely betrothed young man, according to Saeeda's husband. A civil servant of one sort or another.

I locate him in his office, an unprepossessing space, except for a large and ornate nineteenth-century British lavatory protruding almost into the centre of the room. Just why it was placed there defies imagination. Equally obtrusive is a large offering, well past its prime, sitting defiantly in the pan.

Ahmed, a large-nosed, humble sort of fellow, blushes momentarily as we shake hands.

As a getting-to-know-you ritual Ahmed is to take me to visit his 'bride soon'. I am to tell him what I think of her. He himself cannot see her. 'Not allowed.'

We leave the office and walk through alleyways – a hum of feet, greeting and twists and turns.

She is young, rotund and lollipop sweet. 'Very beautiful,' I say to a proud and happy Ahmed, who hasn't ever spoken to his bride to be.

It is the afternoon. I'm in my hotel room. Perhaps it is due to the soulless atmosphere within this hotel, as it has begun to dawn on me just how alone I am. There is no one for me to talk to. No one who understands me. I am friendless in a foreign land, and it's *lonely*.

Fortunately, I have my diary. I extract it from my suitcase, sit at the window. Look out.

Four storeys below me in a small enclosed courtyard are two youths. One is sitting in a wooden wheelbarrow with his legs dangling over its lip while the other holds the barrow's handles and pushes it around.

Around and around.

*Diary*
*Disturbed: This Muslim world – there is something disturbing about it, an*
*indefinable under-the-surface something…*

I lift my head, look down. The youth who had been the passenger is now pushing. Around and around they go.

*Hunger?*
*In the women, in the wives – an enforced invisibility? Saeeda's silence, why?*
*'Platonic love': Saeeda's husband's platonic love among men. Does it also exist here between man and woman?*

The two youths change roles again – the pusher becoming the pushed.

*A male sexual hunger?*

Around and around. So pointless and peaceful. I sit quietly watching, until late shadows draw them in.

Another day. Out in the streets, on my own, with my cameras.

A jumble of open-lidded tin teapots sitting around a small flame reaching up toward a moustached and unsmiling man. A tea maker. There's a boy behind him with a collar of light around his wrist holding his hand to his face in laughter. *Click…*

A back alley, a scattering of boys and men in an alleyway, walled and lined in brick. They move within shadow and light.

Moving quickly, knowing from my experience in Lahore how dangerous it can be to dally. Now I'm in a narrow cobblestoned street.

*Click…* a 'grandmother' with her head covered, her face open, wrapped in a patchwork quilt. A man, a youth pointing a banana, a boy leaning toward the camera. The grandmother's eyes are filled with black.

Another woman, middle-aged, hides her mouth with her hand as I photograph her. Her eyes look out intensely from her mummification of cloth. Beside her, a boy. In front of her, a child's cap. Behind her the lights and shadows give shape to a lad with his hands on his hips and a man pushing his wares.

I move on, the stones smooth beneath my feet.

A soldier, young, soft-shouldered, stands beneath the curves and diamonds of words written on a wall. At the corner a woman hidden in a burka squats, resting. Shadows and light form and reveal a man walking with his hand to his chest in greeting.

A beggar child – a little girl who looks more Indian than Pakistani – sits on an old coat laid out in a yard littered with wood shavings and bits of straw. Silver earrings shine out from a tousle of black hair. Sweets and coins lie around her. Her right hand is cupped, asking for alms. Tucked slightly under the coat, a tiny face, a photograph of a woman. Perhaps it's her mother, or 'dream' mother. I can see from her forming teeth that she must be about eight years old. Her open mouth is an act of theatre, as is her staring expression.

Walking, looking.

*Click*… a man with a vulture's nose and the look of a thief is putting his hand inside his jacket.

A policeman, hands clasped around his knees, sits on a box with a cup of tea, a picture of a llama or stag hanging on a makeshift wall behind him.

My hotel is in sight. I've walked full circle.

A small naked boy climbs the bank of an open sewer in which he has been playing…

Waking slowly next morning I remember a dream I had during the night. An odd little dream: a black, fast-flowing river moon-sparkles, dancing, its shifting current running into a black pool wherein a beautiful boy-child is drowning. I reach out my hand, save him.

Ahmed arrives to chaperone me around his city. Today it is to be 'the heart of Peshawar'. We walk there; vehicles are forbidden.

The street is wide, the mud-brick cobblestones smoothed by time and the tread of feet. Framing the street are six-storey stone houses, leaning inward, the weight of 4000 years, Ahmed tells me, behind them. They cast a permanent shadow on the vendors and browsing humanity below.

The only sound is a low, leisured murmuring.

I'm standing by a fruit stall, running my eyes across the ancient walls of mud-brick and stone. Over the centuries new walls have been built successively on top of old ones.

I look around me. The colours are pastel, soft, the atmosphere so gentle that my feet are reluctant to move, to disturb a dust so alive with – what? Four thousand years of footsteps?

A peculiar sensation; of familiarity and, *at-oneness*… as if I have stepped through Time, back 4000 years. Both in this physical reality, and in my psyche.

Some deep and ancient memory? *A timeslip.* It's biblical; pre-biblical. How wondrously strange. I'm of the modern age yet *feel* as if I belong to this Past. The scent of Human Ages, present.

Catching my breath. Two white eyes as serene as moons are approaching. They're wide with the inward seeing of the blind. His bearded face is impassive, pre-Christ, his body tall, slim, swathed in a rust-red robe. A blood-red turban crowns him; pastel browns surround him.

His long arm is outstretched, fingers clasped around the hand of a tiny boy who is walking in front, leading him. The child is the blind man's eyes.

Levitating by.

Night of the same day. Again with Ahmed, this time wandering through Peshawar's crowded marketplace with my Hasselblad camera.

It's all and only men. Men, surreptitiously brushing against me.

A fruit stall laden with bananas, apples, pomegranates and strange fruits. A boy is laughing, his face and head swathed in white cloth…

We move through the crowd. And as we do bodies push close and a hand snakes around my thigh, trying to grope me from behind. Instinctively I spin, snarl; a hydra of turbaned faces devours me with its eyes.

A Muslim-capped man, face and shoulders only. He's bathed in yellow-brown light, his mouth slightly open. One eye is looking at me, the other is half closed. He's sliding his tongue lasciviously at me… *click.*

# eight

Morning. Muddling about, preparing for an excursion to a gunsmithing village some hours' bus drive from Peshawar.

Knuckles on my door. A stern knock.

I'm surprised to see that it's the Afghan Police Minister. Brushing urgently past me into my room. He's flustered. He's come, he says, to apologise for his wife's behaviour, her 'backwardness'. I place a handful of rolls of film into my carry-bag. Ahmed will soon be here to collect me. The Minister is an unwanted intrusion. 'Please,' I assure him, 'it is of no consequence, and I must now prepare for my day.'

Is he deaf? It's as if he's deaf. He's insisting 'reparation has to be made'. He's boring into my eyes with a mix of apology and pleading... is asking me if I will grant him 'the honour' of being his guest in Afghanistan. A moment's pause, a sliver of interest in his words. Then doubt; his wife doesn't like me. And I do not know him. And I'm not so sure that I want to know him.

'Under my protection you will have access to areas of Afghanistan unreachable by most travellers. I will guarantee this. Many interesting subjects for your photographs.' He's emphatic, almost desperately wanting me to accept.

Areas of Afghanistan unreachable by most travellers. Isn't this what I want?

'I will arrange your bus ticket for tomorrow morning, and meet you at the bus station in Kabul.' He's sealed it. No time for second thoughts.

All the while my placid chaperone, Ahmed, has been sitting on the steps of the hotel. Waiting for me.

We bus out along a narrow mountain road, toward a gunsmithing village pinched between the bouldery slopes of Pakistan's 'ungovernable' Northern Frontier.

Ahmed drops in on a friend while I, amidst the sound of hammers on anvils and watchful eyes, wander up the main street to photograph – a man counting bullets; rows of guns; a gunsmith bent in prayer-like reverence over the barrel of a gun; the sharp suspicious face of a wily-eyed mountain man gawking at me; a child with shadowed eyes and a bandaged finger.

And finally, at the end of the village, a graveyard. It looks as if it could be British, or European. Lost among the stones. The stoned. *Click...*

Late in the night, back in Peshawar, I hear a woman's screams, from somewhere out in the street. Tiptoeing toward the hotel balcony, I conceal myself in the shadows. She is about sixty feet away, near the edge of the open sewer where a day or so earlier I'd photographed a naked boy. She is a writhing worm-like form, a body downed and unable to escape its attacker – a silhouette lunging, punching, kicking.

It's my urge to call out, to stop him. But I'm uncharacteristically timid. Retreat.

## nine

Passivity, the passivity of being a passenger. I like it – it's a protection of sorts. Nothing to do but look out the window and watch the landscape change.

The bus driver, a large, hunch-shouldered serious man, has seated me behind him, thus separating me from the rest of the passengers, a mob of rigidly insular, fiercely staring, suspicious-eyed, turban-wrapped, bearded tribal men.

The bus driver turns the key and the cabin bursts into loud exotic music.

Prickles of excitement; the bus is moving.

The highlands of north Pakistan unfold before me. They are raw, of lunar majesty and isolation: great stony elbows of mountains, mist trapped… spectral shapes.

*Wild.*

Then to my left, rising belligerently from the scarred grey austerity of landscape, a fortress – a *real* fortress – built of orange-brown unbaked brick. It is huge – four, five storeys tall – yet so tiny in comparison to the vast surrounding Nature.

There are gun slits for windows. Is there a whole village – animals et al. – inside?

The Pakistan-Afghanistan border. The bus stops alongside half a dozen others. A group of soldiers approach. They are standing at the bus door. My heart quickens.

I watch as the passengers dismount, scramble onto the roof of the bus and throw the stacked luggage to the ground. Fortunately I have my film and camera cases with me.

The soldiers move off. I dismount, gather my luggage and head toward the end of a long disorganised queue.

Shuffle, shuffle; clouds of small flies, attracted to and trapped among mountains of sultanas.

Hawkers call, children cry, and I watch, my attention caught by small groups of burka-clad women walking across the border, wholly unchallenged.

Shuffle, shuffle, shuffle.

It is now my turn to pass through the customs booth… adrenalin is *rushing* through me, causing a hot sweatiness around a hard flat block tucked into the top of my trousers. It's a slab of 'the peasants' drug', given to me by Ahmed's friend in the very heart of lawlessness itself, the gunsmithing village.

*Why am I doing this?*

Shuffle, shuffle… I'm edging hotly toward the passport officer. Pretend casualness, innocence.

*Fear-thrill.* It is an intense version of the fear-thrill one had as a child knocking on strangers' doors in the night and running away as invisible as the wind when footsteps are heard.

The border guards are picking over my cameras. 'Old, not new,' I tell them.

They scribble something on a piece of paper and put it in my passport. Wave me through. That's it!

Moving on, the bus gear-graunches its way along a mountain trail. My face to the window, nibbling almonds. Gazing out as the bus and the music carry me, hypnotically, onward.

Descending, climbing, descending. Here winter has just finished. The snow has melted, revealing immense naked brown-grey mountain faces. A peculiar unease fills me as I study them. An incomprehensible unease.

Then, as the bus begins to grunt its way up that massive fortress of rock, the Khyber Pass, memory draws back the blinds of forgotten sleeps and I realise, with certainty, *know*, I have been here before; in a dream.

As the bus continues to climb so also does my mind, into the labyrinths of this dream…

Thousands of pilgrims, or refugees, are climbing a long winding road. The mountain sides grey-brown, naked. All are travelling by foot, dressed in exotic flowing clothes, slowly winding our way toward the mountain's summit.

On top the mountain stretches out, forming a plateau upon which an even greater mass of people are gathered, all of whom face to the south-east. I'm turning, facing the opposite direction.

This contrariness disturbs the mass and prompts a passer-by, a man, to come up to me. He asks in a troubled voice: 'Why are you not watching for the explosion?'

With perfect and unshifting calm I dream-reply: 'I have already seen two world wars and wish to see *no more*.'

Upon this utterance, and from the direction in which I am facing, a person approaches me: a long-haired poet dressed in a monk's habit and wearing an expression of infinite loneliness. Coming up to me he looks forlornly at the gathered mass and asks: 'What is it in people that gives them such a capacity for togetherness?'

I smile at him as if at the loveliness of a child. 'It is *illusion*.'

Then fade from this dream.

The bus reaches the top of the Khyber Pass and the summit stretches out onto a high plateau. But here there are traces of winter snow, only just beginning to thaw. Streaked among it are large bold letters. A national greeting?

## ten

*White snows, black crows – cawing, falling through the air. Shimmering stones of mountains high – surrounding, surrounding.*

Disappointment. Kabul is not the charming old-world city of voluptuous mosques and timeless people I'd unwittingly conjured up for myself.

Instead, the bus manoeuvres between a harsh subtopia of 1950s and 60s-style square buildings, equally dull in colour and shape. Tinpot taxis, black military Mercedes and a slush of dirty grey snow fill the drab streets.

We pull into the terminal.

He's here, the Afghan Minister of Police, face flushed with the cold, anonymously waiting. His presence is oddly comforting.

'Welcome to Kabul,' he says as he clutches the handles of my film case and my suitcase. I climb into the soft centrally heated depths of his pearl-grey government-issue Mercedes.

Purring off into a fading light, through flat streets... Toward a set of high gates.

Entering, we park alongside a large austere-looking building which the Minister tells me is a government hotel. The foyer is as forbiddingly impersonal as the hotel's facade. Grim. And extremely cold.

A heat of servant boys leap into action, all smiles and subservience for the Minister who, assuming an air of impatient superiority, instructs them, I presume, as to my needs. It appears that no one speaks English.

Amidst a hush of bodies I sign the register, then am led through a series of long, freezing-cold corridors to a little room at the far end of the hotel.

The Minister orders a pot of tea.

The servant closes the door.

Suddenly, *fright-quick*; the Minister, who a second ago was sitting in the one chair, has dropped to his knees, is professing his love for me. He 'can't sleep, can't eat' (he looks very well fed to me), 'can't think' for love of me.

This is too absurd. Disbelief and consternation shine back at the beseeching brown eyes looking up at me from the flaccid face of this middle-aged, unattractive man. He's *not* play-acting.

I politely splutter that 'it is impossible', 'very sorry', 'only "platonic" friend'.

He registers. His face drops, is thickening, the soft pink flush of devotion fading into a pale grey of rage…

Lungeing at me… pushing, pinning me to the bed, crushing down on me and the block of hashish. His eyes are bulbous, *crazed*, his thick hands diving for my throat.

My mind is lucid: *he's going to strangle me.*

I grab his wrists, with every ounce of strength – *puuuussh.*

My muscles *burning.*

The Minister's face is changing again: purple, grotesque. I'm not strong enough to throw him off, just strong enough to *keep-his-hands-from-my-throat.*

It's working; I'm breaking his resolve. He's rolling himself off me. Heading for and opening the door. A look – a mix of hurt and hate – issues from his eyes. Gone.

I leap up, lock the door. Stunned, totally shocked. I sit. Staring nowhere – no sound, no movement.

Silence.

*Aaargh!* Piercing fright: the teapot lid just moved. It did a little jump. True.

It's night. Too late to open the door and leave. The thought is terrifying. Instead I put myself to bed.

The bedsprings creak at my every movement.

A *sound*. In the wall, just above my head: *scratch-scratch, tap-tap, scratch-scratch, tap-tap*… What is it?

Fingernails! Fingernails scratching the wall of the adjoining room. Slow, deliberate.

Now through the wall opposite, the same *scratch-scratch, tap-tap… They want me.*

Don't move, don't breathe, I tell myself.

My door handle, someone's rattling, pulling it. 'Sigulki, Sigulki!' It's a mouth in the keyhole, the caller's lips squashed, pushing against the metal.

Rattling, scratching, tapping, hissing, and cats crying desperate copulatory screams outside on the frozen ground.

I'm a stone. Stone-still.

Ever so *slowly* the dawn breaks.

## eleven

A youth of about eighteen is behind the hotel's reception desk. I'm shivering and hungry. 'May I have breakfast please? …Food?'

He doesn't speak a word of English. Is reading me with his eyes. I lift my hand to my mouth. 'Food.' He has understood? He disappears, and returns with a tray, bearing a pot of hot tea, a bowl of yogurt, a pancake of unleavened bread, a boiled egg.

I tear the bread. Scoop up a mouthful of yogurt. Cast my eye at the servant, who stands at a small distance, his hands folded in an attitude of modesty and patience.

The yogurt is cool, silken.

I sip three cups of tea. The pot is drained. The servant boy steps toward me, peering at me with large, round guileless eyes.

'Bazaar.' He's asking if I would like to go there.

'Brother.' He's putting his hand to his chest. He is offering to chaperone me there. I accept.

We walk circuitously, keeping to the city's edge. Across a bridge over a broiling glacier-green river, past a small roadside field in which Afghan peasant men are wrestling. We stop to watch the fighters.

I lift my Leicaflex camera to my eye. *Click:* my first image of Afghanistan.

Walking circuitously, keeping to the city's edge…

The bazaar. A sharp scent of spices cuts through the air. My tired-wide eyes stare: coloured curtain-coils of woollen and cotton cloth, shimmering silk. Reels of variously dyed wool and cotton thread, strings of dried fruits, dried skins, bunches of dried herbs. Bulbous-bellied brassware. Rows of open-lidded boxes filled with ground spices. Leather sandals…

Handsome, hook-nosed well-fed merchants haggle, count, weigh, wait, call to the crowds – a kaleidoscopic torrent of cloth and searching faces swirling and eddying in a warm human heat.

The servant boy, my 'brother', leads me through the walls of bodies. He is my bodyguard; stops when I stop, waits by my side as I peruse…

Beads! Thousands of tiny coloured glass and plastic beads, some threaded into exotic-looking necklaces, bracelets, headdresses. That – no, this one – a necklace of hundreds of white, red and translucent beads formed into dozens of interlinked descending triangles leading into one. What patience its maker must have had. *Buy it.* My 'brother' negotiates with the merchant over the price. A small price.

We wander on, I captivated by the mystique, foreign tongues, warm hues and aromatic smells of this enclosed and ancient world: the Kabul bazaar.

Then it's out, into the cold, and a snow-mushy street. Here my 'brother' gestures to me that he has to return to the hotel. I need rest but don't want to spend my day in that ghastly place. I am nervous, but pluck up courage and gesture to the boy to return without me.

I drift back through the city, my camera bag slung across a shoulder. Through a maze of short criss-crossing streets with open-front shops, displaying similar produce to the bazaar, innumerable tea shops, bakeries, fruit and vegetable stalls decorated picturesquely with the wares. Brassware, silverware and small songbirds in cages. A slow, almost static pace.

I extract my camera… walking… looking quietly about me, for faces and images that contain no threat.

*Click:* men with their boy-children sitting and chatting in the wintry sun.

Women encased in burkas gliding about like phantoms, singly, in twosomes, small groups. They're like some high form of mobile art. No flesh in sight, just a blur of soft-coloured dyes and abstract shapes – blue, purple, green, brown, white… gliding through the air.

Fleeing from the camera.

My second night in the poky, miserable room. I have stayed here as I don't know where else to go.

The creak-creaking of my bedsprings is their signal. *Scratch-scratch, tap-tap, whisper-hiss, rattle…*

Last night my fear had been the thought that my persecutors' hands would break through the walls, or pull open the door. But they hadn't. Perhaps they couldn't? If they *couldn't*, need I be afraid?

*Scratch-scratch-scratch, rattle-rattle-rattle…* It's as if they are trying to scratch their way into my nervous system, to haunt me from within.

*Will them away…*

*Click:* a superbly gentle image: pyramids of white flour, falling as fairy snow from a large sieve swinging in the centre of a flour merchant's shop. He's sitting on a wooden box, in profile, smiling, his right hand raised.

I'm in the city, roaming with my cameras through side streets and alleys in what appears to be a bakers' area.

…Rows of unleavened bread, each a stack of about twenty pieces. Behind, a boy wearing a dice-patterned top; behind him, in the shadows, a man kneads dough.

I'm wrapped in my one set of warm clothes – a black woollen pullover, a brown woollen jerkin, and undergarments. A dark blue windbreaker, brown leather gloves, my olive-green snug-fitting woollen trousers, a forest-green scarf, and a blue hand-knitted pompom hat. As usual my face and eyes are free. They have to be.

…Another boy, his head, face and shirt coated in flour. Behind him a complexity of shades, shapes, lines, writing, and the faces of a father and his child turning to look.

Moving on… Moving through.

Click… The white blind eye of a jackal-faced man, more 'seeing' than his seeing eye.

Three waifs, girls, their backs to me, examining something in their hands. The wisdom of the world? One turns, cross-eyed, sees me… *click.*

Passing through a small street a group of young men, a mix of smiles and sourness, lock onto me. Vaguely menacing. I approach, point my camera: one raises his hand and palm toward me, V-ing his fingers. An eye peeping around the corner of the camera frame... I pass by. My technique has worked: casual, my camera as my shield.

…I *catch* an eye the moment it catches mine.

## twelve

*Diary:*
*Indolence, watchfulness – it is so prevalent here, and fills me with a peculiar self-conscious loneliness. Is it cultural alienation, or the way the men stare – invade me with their eyes?*
*What am I to these men? Too blonde, too bold? Know-realise that this artist, wanderer, is an outsider. Untouchable!*
*In the presence of the blind I feel free.*

My third night in the government hotel and there is the same demented wall *scratching* keyhole *whispering* door *rattling* carry-on, but it no longer quickens me with fear. An indication that I have recovered a measure of confidence.

Morning. Clarity has returned. I remember that one of the few sensible precautions I'd taken prior to flinging myself across the world into this unknown was to buy a map of Afghanistan. I had forgotten I had it. I pull it out.

It has some useful information on the back:

Geography: …a landlocked country enclosed by a stupendously wild geography, centrally positioned between the Middle East, the Indian Subcontinent, Central Asia and the Far East…

Population: …estimated at nineteen million; a patchwork quilt of ethnic and linguistic groups, criss-crossed by mountain ranges up to 6000 metres and imbued with an anarchic sense of tribal independence.

Language: …two main languages – a Persian dialect similar to the Farsi spoken in

Iran, and Pashto. Persian is the language applied to the government and officials.

Agriculture: …wheat, barley, peas, rice, millet and maize are the most important crops. Pomegranates, citrus fruit, grapes, melons, almonds and cashew nuts…

History: …situated in the very heart of the Asiatic continent, Afghanistan not only presents the most wild and sublime scenery in the world but also one of the most turbulent histories. Coined the 'roundabout civilisation' Afghanistan has been the centre of empires, and a centre for the reception and diffusion of religious and artistic forms all over Asia; from the ancient Mother Goddess cults of the Upper Palaeolithic through to Classical, Buddhist, Hindu, and the present Islamic period. It was here that the Vedas were composed; where Buddhism knew its greatest flowering; and where legend speaks of a concentration of 'knowledge' or 'mystery' held within this land and its peoples…

A tap on the door. It is the servant boy – my 'brother' – with my breakfast. Just the person. I open up the map.

'Kandahar,' he volunteers, with a bright certainty.

I scan the map for Kandahar. There are two major roads, which link in a loop around a large patch of striated brown – a massive mountain range, the Hindu Kush.

I follow the straighter road, read the names: Ghazni, Mushaki, Shah Juy, Qalat, Jaldak, Kandahar.

'There. Kandahar,' I point to the map.

He peers at the spot where my finger is and his eyes light up. 'Kandahar. Good.'

The bus station: a circus of people, bizarrely painted buses, me and my 'servant brother'. My ticket purchased, my luggage stacked safely, he sees to it that I am given a seat at the front.

We say goodbye. 'Good people. Bad people.' He's looking at me, telling me with his eyes that he knew of my torment, that in his brotherly way he had been my protector.

Someone has slipped into the seat next to me. A man, about forty, wearing a shabby but clean suit. He doesn't return my stare. I turn back to my 'brother'…

The bus motor starts. His smiling face is still looking up at mine… following me with his eyes and smile… beyond sight. I don't even know his name.

The bus moves out and as it does I snatch a quick glance behind me at the other passengers. Wild men: turbaned, wrapped in layers of traditional garments, their faces embellished with heavy beards. Sharp, semi-Hebraic noses. Kohl-rimmed death-defiant eyes, hashish-red. Hooked on mine.

A pungent intestinal gas filters foully along the aisle.

A little way into our journey, and in the middle of a flat scrubby wasteland, the bus stops and disgorges its dishevelled occupants, who in unison crouch and relieve their bladders.

Then they stand, forming rows.

Bend to the ice-hard ground.

Kiss the earth.

Raise their hands to the sky.

Stand.

Kneel.

Bow.

*Pray.*

Beyond these praying forms the grey-purple earth reaches out to a distant and jagged line of hills jutting blackly against a grey, rain-weighted sky. East? The direction of Mecca?

Their ritual is humbling and reminds me of the yellow-robed backs bent in prayer in the mosque in Lahore.

The men file back into the bus – leering dementedly at me as they pass my seat, crushing my respect for their obviously only momentary submission to 'the spirit'. Is it my blonde hair, blue eyes? Or because my head is uncovered?

But I cherish my foreignness, my individuality, my right to be me, no matter where.

We're moving, but the landscape is unchanging: distant black-jagged hills and a cold, grey-purple earth littered with stones, scraggly leafless bushes and a sense of desolation...

*This land, Afghanistan – time frozen? Trapped in the echoes of a history choked on its own and savage fullness?*

Jackdaws, ravens – crows? Scatterings of them fly clumsily, distracting me from my thoughts.

Three to four hours of travelling and the bus stops again, again disgorging its occupants who again relieve their bladders, kiss the earth, pray. All this time the man next to me has sat so quietly, not leaving the bus to join the others in prayer nor moving as much as a finger. His composure has aroused my curiosity.

I interrupt our peace, look at him. He turns on my glance. Shyly. I introduce myself. From his expression it's as if he has been waiting for me to do so.

'Mr John.' It's all the English his quiet voice appears to own. Is it his real name?

He reaches inside his worn jacket, extracting a thin brown-red book, his passport. It is Afghan. He opens it and shows me the photograph of himself. Is flicking through the pages so that I can see the stamps.

He touches his heart. 'Traveller.'

A warm endlessness resonates through my being. It is the way in which he spoke the word, *traveller*.

I sneak a peek at the profile of his weather-worn, faraway face; a map of lines, hills, mountains and deserts. Destinations. His skin a warm brown of summer earth.

Aware that I am looking at him, Mr John stares at his knees, a wisp of a smile showing at the corner of his mouth. He is self-contained.

Safe.

The men reboard the bus, and again fix on me as they file past. I gaze out of the window, in time to see a weasel darting across the frozen earth. So wild, so free!

Crows, ravens, jackdaws – only the crow family appears to inhabit this territory.

*Kandahar.* The bus motor switches off. The head-splittingly loud music stops. It's dark. Where in the world am I? Nervous apprehension, insecurity. Where am I going to stay?

Mr John stands up, looking at me. 'Hotel?'

I shrug my shoulders: 'No.' My voice sounds timid.

'Come.'

I follow Mr John out of the bus and into a taxi stripped of all affectations but its seats.

A little bumpiness later and I am standing in the foyer of a cheap but cosy-looking hotel.

'Tomorrow, 9am,' Mr John says, and disappears.

# thirteen

Laughter and the shrill joy of children playing greets my new day. I've slept well.

The morning sun is warm, warmer than Kabul.

I'm outside, standing by the hotel's small gate, waiting. Here spring is aburst – a coquettish prettiness of pink-white blossoms.

On the dot of nine Mr John greets me. Shyly he asks if I want to see the bazaar.

It is quite different from Kabul's – more specialised. We pick our way through to its heart, the world of the Muslim craftsmen – a small city of tinsmiths, of squatting bodies busily bent hammering and handcrafting tin pots, tin cups, tin trunks, tin this, tin that.

Sharp lights, sharp darks and such a noise in this metallurgist's haven. I wince at the clamour. It is impossible to hear myself think, to see to photograph anything.

Moving on, we wander through the streets, Mr John stopping and waiting patiently as I photograph rumble-tumble-looking shops and their keepers as impressively immobile... *click...* as their stocks of cigarettes and '7-o'clock' shaving blades.

For some reason I intuitively trust my silent stranger friend, Mr John. He possesses an inner quiet. Unlike myself. I have a question I've been battling with for a few hours now. It has to do with my taste for the 'exotic', to enter this culture, its atmospheres, through the osmosis of the altered state. Dare I?

Mr John, turning, pulls a face at me, mocking my obviously pained expression. I feel as serious as a judge about to pass sentence.

'Hashish?' The word simply pops out.

Doubt flits across Mr John's features. He glances hesitantly at me, a look of concern and disappointment in his eyes. I feel foolish.

We walk on. Silent.

He's slowing down... We're walking toward a shabby grocery store. Mr John is speaking to the shopkeeper, who invites us in. He locks the door.

The shopkeeper leads us through his shop, gestures to us to sit and disappears into an alcove at the back. Almost immediately there is the sound of a small Primus stove firing up. Tea? I settle on my seat. Look around.

His shop is dirty, with the unkemptness of any old man's back garage. But is atmospheric, cosy. My eyes move into the shadows and spy a grubby little girl sitting in a corner. She's clutching a dishevelled baby blackbird… it's looking at me: black-innocent eyes, liquid-soft, alert. Unblinking. The girl stares fixedly beyond me to where the shopkeeper has disappeared. She's afraid. The baby blackbird not.

The shopkeeper reappears with a pot of tea, glasses, and an old biscuit tin. He prises open the lid and spoons a greenish-yellow powder onto the palm of his hand. Crushed biscuits? He closes his hands together and slowly, rhythmically, rubs them.

Five minutes later he opens his hands, revealing a black-green puttyish mass. Crumbling it, he tips it into one of those hubble-bubble pipes from *Arabian Nights*.

The shopkeeper pours us each a glass of tea, lights the pipe. *Hashish!* He passes the pipe to me. I inhale deeply, this time without coughing. A cool quiet pervades.

The men begin to talk to each other, heads bowed and bent together.

The hashish has taken effect: the room has become enclosing – too dark and lifeless. I want to go.

I stand up to leave.

What does he want? Why is he pinning me down with his knowing eyes, tapping the tin?

'Ten thousand afghani.' The shopkeeper wants me to buy it. I peer in. A subtle green-yellow; sunshine and spring intermixed.

A soporific feeling, endless bliss floods through me.

Sunlight. Sunlight folds me in dusty yellow, warm-clear. *Space.*

A wide earthen street. Handsome and self-assured men, robed and turbaned. Deep reds, greens, blues… flowing, flowing. Into 'Old Time'. *Dissolving.*

## fourteen

Mid-afternoon and the sun is streaming into my hotel room. The exquisite effect of the hashish has begun to diminish. I want more. I love its magic.

I break off an edge of my Peshawar lump, crumbling it, roll it into a cigarette…

Lying back on my bed, wrapped in sunlight, warm indolence…

*Heavenly.*

I lazily turn my hand. A tiny flash of light bounces across the room. It has darted out from the black 'star sapphire' embedded in the head of my soul-symbol – a lioness-bodied, serpent-tailed, eagle-winged, human-faced sphinx on a ring on my middle left finger.

My attention captured by this tiny light, I draw it across the walls towards and onto my face, and play; twist and turn my sphinx and her shining jewel…

To try to *catch* the light in my eyes…

*Uzait!* Blindness, blinding *light*.

*Thump.* My door. Booted open. Two soldiers. Leering in.

Stabs of fear…

Without a word they turn and close the door.

The hashish is sitting on the table in the middle of the room. They must have seen it!

Thudding footsteps. Are they coming back? To arrest me?

Thudding footsteps… going past.

I wait. Nothing. But I must find out why they came.

I'm at the top of the stairs, looking down toward the hotel's reception room. It is full of young Afghan men dressed in Western clothes, their attention fixed on an extraordinarily handsome, charismatic man standing in their midst. They are talking animatedly to him.

Too nervous to intrude.

A servant comes along the corridor toward me but he doesn't understand what I'm trying to ask. I give up, go back.

A tapping at my door. A soft unobtrusive tapping. I open my door. Onto eyes, his eyes… those of the elegant man from the reception area. Proud and serene they hold me in a state of transfixed calm as he tells me that he is the owner of the hotel. That the soldiers were looking for a junkie tourist who had been stealing from the local shops. He's very courteous. Softly spoken.

'My name is Assilan. It translates as "the Lion". I'm a student of medicine and I normally live in Kabul. I'm visiting Kandahar as I have to fulfil my duties as a landlord.'

A carefully combed black beard. Wavy hair falling to the line of his jacket collar. And a face type that I have not yet encountered: soft, moon-shaped, it exudes a courtly air, aristocratic, like that of a prince in a Persian miniature, shadowless.

He's looking at me, waiting for me to speak.

To speak! I have not spoken for so long.

'I'm Victoria. I'm a photographer, and traveller,' I say, relieved beyond measure.

We converse outside my room – about photography. He has a camera that he has bought from a tourist. A Nikon. He wants to know if it is a good model. I confess I don't know much about this type of camera, but that does not matter, the question is merely an entrée into conversation.

Soon Assilan is educating me about his country, the system of land ownership. It is a feudal system, and he is a landowner, and landlord, a caretaker of tribal peoples, who have traditional rights of occupancy on his land. The rents they pay to him allow him to achieve his chosen role; to be a scholar and person of learning. He describes a system of mutual dependency and protection, not the dominance and exploitation that I, from my school history lessons, understood feudalism to be.

Kandahar is the ancient seat of the Afghan kings and was founded by Alexander the Great, Assilan tells me.

I'm fascinated, by him as much as by what he is telling me. But I am also worried, thinking about the hashish on my table. And the soldiers. I need to be reassured. I ask Assilan what he knows of its tradition.

'Hashish is made from the pollen of the marijuana plant. It is not illegal – alcohol is. The village people grow it on my lands, for their own uses. It has a 5000-year history as a medicament for chronic pain, as an aphrodisiac, for sleep or creativity. And for courage.'

Assilan continues, telling me that the drug is an integral part of the Muslim tradition, the men in Afghanistan smoking it from a young age.

He speaks with a slight lisp – all his s's soft.

Assilan wants to know what brings me to Afghanistan.

'I am interested in Afghanistan's face – its people. And exploring,' I tell him.

He has a suggestion.

'It would be good, for your photographic aims, to visit the city of Mazar-e-Sharif. It is in Afghan Turkestan, in the north. It is a holy city, the holy shrine, and one of Islam's great places of pilgrimage. In about one week hundreds of thousands of pilgrims from all over Afghanistan, the Middle East and Pakistan will gather to honour the Prophet Muhammad and his disciple Ali, and celebrate the Islamic New Year. The new lunar year. It would be very interesting for you.'

I'm lost in his eyes. Deep, soft-black, and masculinely sure, they possess, in both their shape and expression, a languid, soulful intelligence.

He's to return to Kabul tomorrow. Would I like to accompany him?

I'm drawn to him. But I have only just arrived here. I'll stay.

He gives me his telephone number in Kabul. With a gentle bow of his head says goodbye. I quietly close the door. Dazzled.


## fifteen


Hidden in my clothes in the back of my suitcase is a folding knife. I brought it with me for practical purposes and also for my security. I can't find it. It has vanished.

Who could have taken it? How? When?

On the morning Mr John and I roamed the bazaar – that is the only time it could have been taken. The soldiers?

The junkie tourist.

His room is somewhere along the hallway, I'm told.

I rap authoritatively on a randomly selected door. A haggardly thin young European man answers, stares at me pathetically. 'You have my knife?' I ask accusingly.

'Yes,' his simple confession.

I feel mean taking it, he looks so tragic. But then he had stolen into my locked room.

A few days have passed, spent roaming around the area of my hotel, photographing the merchants and street life, Mr John, my godsend, always patiently there. It has made photographing much easier.

I have decided to follow Assilan's advice and travel to Mazar-e-Sharif. Besides, I do not feel comfortable knowing that my door can be opened by others. They could steal my cameras.

On my last day I spend the morning in 'almond blossom thoughts'. The season here is, I've realised, the opposite to that of my sunset-summer home country.

Mr John appears at the hotel gate in the mid-late afternoon. We're to go for a 'walk', to meet his 'friend'.

We stroll through to the outskirts of Kandahar city. The weather is balmy, relaxing. Within half a mile smooth-sided mud walls and silence replace the hum of dusty streets and commerce.

A while on we reach what I assume is the meeting place, a flat, deserted area spreading away into a low-lying purplish haze ringed by silhouettes of sphinxian hills haloed by a molten sky. Within this mystical landscape we wait.

Half an hour ticks by: no friend. Mr John leads me around an area of walled-in houses. We walk, circle upon circle, around and around. No words.

Then from the silence the sound of hoofs… closer… thundering through the walls… emerging; a magnificent black stallion: head high, nostrils flared, galloping across our path, a flash of gold bronze light in its wide black eyes. Coloured ribbons stream from its braided mane. Its tail is high, bound and tasselled.

A whip cracks the air. Behind, in a painted carriage from the age of the gladiators, is the standing form of a man robed and turbaned in a proud shade of purple, eyes to the fore, chiselled face to the setting sun.

The apparition speeds past – 2000 years past. The red dust settles. Circle upon circle, upon circle.

I glance covertly up at Mr John. His eyes are lowered and he is wearing that wide-hidden expression I'd noticed on numerous occasions. He is youngish yet so old. *Secretive.* Who is he? A spy, or messenger of some sort? A secret-keeper?

And why are we here?

He reads my mind; turns toward me, smiles his wonderful desert-earth smile. Calmed, my thoughts fold into like reply.

Eventually a brown-hooded figure approaches from the distance. It's Mr John's friend. We meet beneath a cracked mud wall on top of which a young girl sits, watching.

The men bow to each other and, without lifting their faces, exchange greetings. They reassume upright postures, reach out their arms, touch each other's shoulders and pull together to kiss each other on the cheek.

Mr John, his hands joined as in prayer, drops to his knees, bends to the earth, and kisses his friend's feet. *Sublime.*

The two men talk. I see the friend pass something to Mr John. They part.

A blazing orange-gold light and scintillas of dancing red dust form our path as Mr John and I stroll back.

It is evening when we reach the hotel gate.

Bidding me farewell, Mr John slips me a small brown paper package. He joins his hands, bows slightly and is gone, a shadow in the night.

## sixteen

Again I am not to be alone in my front seat in the bus. The only other passenger wearing Western clothes is seated next to me. He's an Afghan and, like Mr John, quiet. Unlike Mr John he is well dressed and manicured. We politely acknowledge each other.

Rumbling across a wide, nondescript plain toward an unseen mountain range – the jagged peaks of the Hindu Kush.

The bus, beginning its ascent, snakes between mountain-hugging and shadowed valleys, narrower and narrower as we climb.

We pass a cluster of stone-pile houses – a whole village – clinging miraculously to the sheer, ice-walled rock of the mountainside.

Up, up into an eye-blistering light of godly heights; of snow-softly folding sky and land in equal blinding measure. Here the road becomes a slippery mush of hidden ice: the bus slithers, grinds forward… through… White… into Black, a tunnel – a stinging, suffocating fog. An airless tomb cut through the mountain's peak. This is the Salang Tunnel.

Out again… I see only white.

The bus dips, winds, dips. Dipping now sharply down

down

sharply down

into an ever-widening valley of fields frilled and dotted with the pink of blossoming almond trees. The Hindu Kush is behind us, a vast white spine now picturesque rather than forbidding.

We stop for a rest, drink tea, stretch our legs. Recover.

I savour the delicacy of the surrounding nature. The remote fairy-story landscape, the white thighs of grand mountains stretching away into the distance, the air sweet with the scent of willows.

We are moving on. Fast and sure now, the bus, fleeing the mountains, enters a gentle undulation of landscapes touched with round red-mud houses, woolly black fat-tailed sheep and a perfect green.

Abruptly, the scene changes and a sky-stretching desert looms... *Flatness* – as far as the eye can see. To the edge of the world? In a light panic I scan the desert for life... There, way away on the horizon, a tiny but moving dot. It's a camel train.

Night bleeds across the desert. At breakneck speed we head toward a distant beacon of light. 'Mazar-e-Sharif,' announces the manicured man sitting next to me.

We have conversed intermittently during our journey. He tells me he works for the World Scout Organisation, speaks eight languages and travels the world throughout the year. He has come home to celebrate the Muslim New Year.

The bus slows as we enter the sparsely lit city of Mazar-e-Sharif, finally growling and shuddering to a stop.

'There are no tourist facilities here,' the scoutmaster tells me. 'Accommodation will be very scarce. But I know one hotel that will have a room. I will tell the driver where to take you.'

The driver's assistant steps down and opens the door. Immediately a stampede sounds from behind me. A blur of bodies rushing from the back of the bus disappears into the night.

I'm last off. 'Joy of joys,' I manage to utter through gritted teeth as ankle-high mud and horse dung icily fill my shoes. The freezing wind is filled with needle-sharp ice-splinters. Piercing.

Teeth tight. Eyes shut.

Slosh, slosh, slosh.

I heave my luggage onto a horse cart. An aloof and composed scoutmaster is telling the driver where to take me.

The hotel is dirty, cold and appears to be run by young men whose only communication is the loud back-sucking of nasal mucus. They snottily crowd about me as I sign the register. 'Nama, nama?'

'Queen Victoria,' I say coldly and with untouchable superiority, aware that my feet have turned to frozen dung.

'Queen Victoria.' They repeat it perfectly.

Armoured in queenly hauteur, I order the servants to carry my luggage to my room, where I lock the door with a soundless laugh.

Then it strikes me: gnawing hunger. I'm achingly hungry, and the hotel only does breakfast. There's no choice; I'm going to have to go back… out… into the *freezing* night.

There are no street lights and I have no torch. But somehow, in the middle of a dark nowhere I find a broken-timbered, doorless eating house.

In my muddy wet shoes I step onto its muddy floor, looking around and spying an empty seat at the end of a long bench.

The eating house is full of males, their ravaged ravenous bodies hunched as they stab dirt-ingrained fingers into their bowls and shovel globs of steaming mush into their black-toothed or wholly toothless mouths. Turban-wrapped, black-bearded men who haven't noticed me. Does the steam rising from their wet clothes, the food, render me invisible? Or is it my pompom hat, and the mountain of clothes I'm wearing?

Without my asking, a steaming grey gruel consisting of meat, rice and fat is placed roughly on the table before me.

I am momentarily wary, but too hungry. I join the others, finger-spooning my way hotly, greedily, down to the layer of sludge at the bottom of the bowl.

My dinner, I am soon to discover, is dangerously populated. In the morning I have excruciating stomach cramps and cannot get out of bed. I reach for my lump of hashish, the 'medicament for chronic pain'.

*Diary:*
*Rain pours, cold blows, comfortingly*
*outside.*
*Camels nonchalantly clomp on muddied streets*
*below.*
*Horses and drays tinkle past.*
*Voices murmuring in the night,*
*the Muezzins call. Low, High,*

*Hypnotic, Monotonous,*
*Levitating,*
*Light,*
*shivers.*
*A river of treading feet passes steadily by.*

## seventeen

I am ill for three days. The first day of sunshine I'm up, and out.

White pigeons, rising,

falling,

as a cloud, *angel soft*, rising again.

Behind them is a celestial blue and gold (silvery white in certain lights), voluptuously domed, elegantly minareted mosque. The 'Blue Mosque', or 'Tomb of Ali' according to what the scoutmaster had told me, and Mazar-e-Sharif's soul reason.

Release – inspiring, uplifting transcendent release in its Ishtar-ish crescent-moon-crowned beauty. Its bedazzlement of exquisite patterns and colours; mosaics of blue, primarily blue, into turquoise-aquamarine, white, yellow, black. As countless as the stars.

Is this why the pilgrims come here – are amassing in their thousands? They raise their hands and bow their heads, moving as a holy tide.

Inside? I don't know. The minders don't let me – an 'unbeliever' – near the mosque's door. I'm so obviously different, a free-faced outsider, individual.

As are the maimed, who must have been brought here, and who are stationed all around the vicinity of the mosque. I feel an affinity with them: the blind, limbless, faceless, mindless, misplaced, old and young, *no longer human*, sitting, slumping, wriggling in blanketed deformity. Victims of syphilis, leprosy, war, or conception; equally alone.

What was it I read somewhere? 'Perhaps if one wishes to remain an individual in the midst of the teeming multitudes one must make oneself grotesque.'

I see him, some distance away, on the other side of an open drain, a footbridge filled with passers-by to his right, a crowd surging behind him. He is about eighteen, legless, his face from nose to chin a scar of skinless, twisted flesh. His mouth lipless; a toothless fleshy hole.

He's seen me, although I am quite far away. He's running away on the palms of his hands, down into a ditch. I gently move closer, look down. His head is clamped into his chest. He is hiding from me. Trying to hide his terrible deformity. My heart fills with compassion for him.

Another. He has hair, two seeing eyes, two holes for a nose, three jagged teeth protruding from the bone of a fleshless mouth, a white-brown and shattered bone of a chin. One limb is missing. I photograph him.

A blind man wrapped in a grey blanket and wearing a dark blue turban sits on the cold earth with his legs folded crookedly. Behind him, a white tomb. He fingers prayer beads… *click*.

A boy. I'm a few yards from him. Pilgrims flow between us, the mosque out of focus behind him.

Neither of us moves. I'm drawn, stare-struck by his eyes. They're completely red. And have no pupils. I feel a sadness for him – his innocent face, so fixed, unknowing, emanates the grace of a bird in flight.

He *knows* that I'm here. He's opening his mouth, beaming me a most Divine smile, is *filling* me with it. Stunned by his loveliness I move away. But how could that blind child have seen/known me?

Within the night's shroud, anonymity. This is the wisest time to move, to be among the crowds of pilgrims circling the 'Tomb of Ali'. I want to know, to feel the mass.

It's *cold*, so cold that the mud of day is now black splinters of ice. The mass is as shadow forms; soundless and obedient. About halfway around the mosque and the cold has begun to shrink into my bones. I can feel my skeleton.

Perhaps it is my freezing bones that opens my vision to the night and singles out a figure amidst the passing crowds. He is tall, barefooted and wearing nothing more than a thin cloak. How ludicrous, I think to myself, for someone to so deliberately torture themselves for the sake of religion. What a stupidly foolish man.

As we pass I look up into the pilgrim's face and am filled with shock and shame. It is the worldly scout master who had sat next to me on the bus!

He doesn't see me; his vision is fixed inward, clothed in mystical calm. In the face of this asceticism I lower my gaze, feeling profoundly self-conscious.

*Earthbound.*

Perhaps there is a higher order, a higher plane of knowing after all.

The New Year is creeping forward, and as it does Mazar-e-Sharif has begun to show signs of bursting. The crowd is a crush and the mosque, the area the pilgrims seek, is almost impossible to move around. I remain the only blond, blue-eyed person in this enormous crowd of dark-haired, dark-eyed worshippers.

I seek and keep to the perimeter. Cameras at the ready.

Two women kneel on patterns of dark grey stone spanning out from the mosque, their bodies concealed in burkas. For modesty *and* safety? They're at prayer, or soaking up the brief warmth offered by the sun… *click.*

Lines of men, kneeling, praying beneath a cold sharp sun. A single bare foot. A child's face poking over the rows of buttocks.

White pigeons. Hundreds alight – rising from the grain-filled palms of pilgrims, circling as a cloud of wings around the gold-tipped minarets of the Blue Mosque, the 'Tomb of Ali'.

A shoe minder with his knees tucked under him, the mosque behind him. His hand is wrapped in wool and he holds a stick. Body and face are wrapped against the cold. Ten pairs of mud-covered shoes, from rubber galoshes to traditional toe-turned embroidered leather slippers, sit facing him…

A back view of two pilgrims walking. The one closest carries a large bundle of belongings on his head…

Three soldiers holding hands. The one in the middle is the best dressed, the important one. Another has a gentle face, the third looks a touch retarded…

A squatting woman, about my age, sits hunched against the icy wind. Her black hair billows about her naked wild face, her desert nomad's fiercely proud green eyes holding mine.

Eyes, so many. Is it the absence of language that draws me to them? In this 'visual' connection there is a sense of communication; as I too stare, a part of me fascinated and hungry for affirmation of my human belonging.

But it is eyes at odds that are of increasing fascination…

The blind, the maimed, and the red-eyed blind boy are nowhere to be seen, they have disappeared into an ocean of bodies broiling with religious fervour. God thought. It's scary, feels dangerous. Time to go.

Bussing across the desert. Back across through the valleys of green and pink, and round fairy-tale houses.

The mountain pass is sheer torture: treacherous weather and an immense traffic jam at the entrance to the tunnel.

Headlights and fog; a choking coughing *suffocating* thick black fog of diesel exhaust. Bus horns honking, bleating, moaning… I'm trying to breathe through my scarf… chest thick, choking… how much longer?

At last, dizzy, sweaty and half dead, we emerge.

A chain of souls – countless disembodied, expressionless-staring faces through the window; dark-haired men from generals dressed in starched uniforms and mirror sunglasses inside black Mercedes to rag-wrapped beggars in donkey-drawn carts – thousands and thousands of pilgrims, wending, inch by surreal inch, toward Mazar-e-Sharif. To celebrate the birth of Islam.

The few women are all scrupulously, wholly covered.

I am from another planet.

## eighteen

Kabul has changed in my relatively short time away. It's busy, warm, spring-ripe. And full of tourists: Swedes, Danes, French, Americans. The generation of Bob Dylan's 'Tangled up in Blue' – hippies, druggies, seekers – they crowd into the tea shops, filter along the inner-city streets, while away the hours caught in the romance, one another, a strange land.

Kabul in spring, it seems, is the 'in' place for this – my – generation.

Is it a twinge of envy I feel upon seeing some of them, obviously overlanders, cruising off together in their sticker-decorated landcruisers? Where are they going? The Sapphire Lake at Band-i-Amir? The jewelled oasis of Nimla? The terrifying defiles of the Jagdalak Pass? The cliff caves and giant, atemporal eyed Buddhas of Bamiyan? The skeleton cities of Hadda or Shar-i-Zohak? To bow before the great stupas of the Jalalabad Plain?

I should feel reassured by the presence of these newcomers but instead I feel more estranged from them than from the people who live here. It is a disconcerting feeling: I share the same hair, skin, eye colour and sometimes language. And definitely the same foreignness. But to me they are intimidating, distant.

I avoid going into the cafes where they congregate.

Instead, in search of photographic images, I wander through Kabul's back streets into an area of high mud-stone walls and mud-slime streets.

*Click...* a man pissing on the crumbling brick wall.

...two men in a back street.

...a boy within shadow and light.

...a soldier leaning against a wall.

...two women simultaneously half-hiding half-staring at me through the threaded grills imprisoning their faces, their eyes.

...the walls, the shadows, the hardship, the illusionless aesthetics of poverty.

Walking back. Thinking that – *military police?... click* – it is time for me to leave, to book my flight back to India. I want to visit Kashmir. I am told it is the Venice of India, a place of water and ease. It will be an excellent contrast to this black-white, geographically 'schismatic' – raw and refined, brutal and beautiful – very grand land.

I'm also culturally fatigued. This has not been an easy country to travel alone in. I need time out, away from the ever-present watchfulness of its people, the hungry stares of its menfolk.

I book my ticket. In four days I go. I'm now free to relax, to be myself.

Assilan, the calming-charming hotel owner I met in Kandahar, comes to mind. I would like to meet him again.

I telephone him.

A voice answers in Persian. Quiet and mannerly. Again, that inexplicable sense of peace. Assilan, the lion, has been waiting for my call. We arrange to meet on a street close to where I'm staying.

Noise: street noise, the clutter of traffic, passers-by. I'm standing waiting near a closed money changer's booth.

He's threading his way through the crowd toward me. Is *shimmering* – gold and silver. His aura? Or the angle of light?

He's seen me. Is smiling. An effervescent energy awakens in me: attraction? He draws close. Divine eyes gently greet mine.

We stroll through the throng, chatting, mutually pleased to see each other. I tell him of my imminent departure while sipping a glass of mint-flavoured tea in a little backstreet tea shop, or 'chai shop' as they are locally known.

'Four days – it is such a brief time in which to know and share oneself with a friend,' he says. Assilan wishes to share these last days with me. To entertain me.

He takes me on a tour of some of Kabul's carpet factories – a collection of small rooms wherein I observe the tiny fingers of girl-children weaving spider-like between thread and loom.

He introduces me to his polite, immaculately dressed upper-class student friends. They are delicate, manicured and highly articulate, and I must make sure I dot my i's and cross my t's. At times beguiled by my own somewhat cracked noblesse.

For my last night in Afghanistan Assilan invites me to partner him to Kabul's exclusive nightclub. I learn that this is the modern way of celebrating the birth of Islam, the year (622) when the prophet Muhammad set forth to disseminate the word of Allah. The date of the Moslem Lunar calendar and their New Year is known as Hijira, flight.

The day of the night of the New Year.

I'm excited – but what to wear? The clothes I have with me are not particularly suitable for an evening out with Afghanistan's aristocracy: only one reasonable Indian cotton dress. Which would pass if I wore stockings. But where, in this city, might I find stockings? I have an excuse to phone Assilan.

He knows where to find ladies' stockings and graciously insists he accompany me to *the* shop. But he doesn't have much time, as he's about to go off and investigate a rumour concerning 'a find of gold coins dating back to the days of the Roman Empire'.

How appropriately odd, our fingering our way through these loose piles of silken things, comparing their tonal values and sheen. A suitable pair is agreed upon.

Early evening. A black-suited Assilan – his wave of hair and beard freshly combed and oiled, an open-necked red silk shirt revealing manly black curls – has arrived to escort me to the nightclub. As I had scanned him, he scans me – my face – my lipsticked lips. He looks very pleased.

'Gold coins?' I ask.

'Yes. They were in a valley outside of Kabul. In an area usually avoided as it is believed to be the dwelling place of a djinn.'

'What is a djinn?' I ask, quietly amused, as the way he said it is the way people often mispronounce my surname.

The djinn are mythical beings, or spirits, and are created from fire. They hold supernatural powers and are usually invisible, but can appear in visible forms, sometimes in the shape of a whirlwind in the desert, or a serpent or human being. It is believed that there are both good and evil djinn; the evil ones often appearing in the form of a hideous old hag, the good ones in the form of a 'resplendently handsome man', Assilan tells me, a small teasing smile upon his resplendently handsome face.

'Basically though,' he assures me, 'this belief is a superstition spread by the village people, as a way to keep foreigners away from their lands, and areas of hidden and buried riches. The djinn supposedly inhabiting the valley I visited is apparently an evil one. But we didn't meet.'

We set out into the night, sitting close together in the back seat of the taxi, silent and aware of the mingling of our perfumes: Assilan's a pleasant, slightly ticklish spicy-sweet musk oil; mine the light and delicate fragrance of Joy.

Apart from the Middle-Eastern handsomeness of my escort and that of a crowd of other Afghans, all dressed in Europe's latest fashions, I could be in any strobe-flashing, drum-thudding nightclub anywhere in the world. The atmosphere is alive, buzzing, enticing us to dance.

It's Western-style: gyrating, hip-swinging, twirling, foot-playing in a pleasant tease of formal sensuality. Surrounding us, a plethora of bodies and wafting perfumes.

Two, three dances and I'm heating up. We're now both puffed, and enjoying each other.

Then – sixth sense? – I glance beyond Assilan's smiling face. Straight into a pair of unforgettable brown eyes, those of the Police Minister, who is dancing with his wife.

Right next to us!

I break my step – momentarily. I must pretend I haven't seen him.

Assilan has noticed my discomfort. 'Don't worry,' he says reassuringly. He has no idea of the cause of my distress.

I draw a mask over the moment, recover my swing until the band stops.

Back at our table Assilan's friends are interested in me – my travels, my plans, my person. I'm a novelty to them, a stranger from a distant part of the world, and I am suddenly sorry that I shall be leaving Afghanistan the next morning. There are unexpected and touching exclamations of 'How sad it is that you are leaving just as friendships are forming.'

'Yes, it is sad,' I reply. And it is. I like these refined and educated people.

Our seats have high backs, designed for privacy. The lighting is nightclub dim. But not so dim that I can't see – *heart-sink* – the Minister of Police, arising doom-like from the next table. He must have overheard every word I've said.

Midnight, the day of New Year is over and it is time to go. Assilan escorts me back to my hotel. I invite him to my room for a farewell chat; a pleasant way to round off the evening, and get to know this man a little more…

During our conversation – my questions about his country's culture, which this gentle man obligingly answers – he speaks about his ambitions and ideals. 'I want to be a doctor and to serve humanity. I have one year more of study, then I shall be qualified. I will be twenty-eight when I am finished – six years of study in all.'

My eyes glide over his mouth, the sensuous dip and curve of his upper lip, the black line of kohl running along its masculine rim.

Am I, have I fallen in love with him?

He's changing the subject. His voice is high. 'In Afghanistan, a woman who has blonde hair and blue eyes is likened to a diamond, rare and beautiful…'

*Buddha eyes,* serenely enveloping mine…

Silence. We are aware.

He shifts. 'Here, I have gift for you.' He slips his hand inside his jacket and withdraws a small glass jar, filled with a honey-gold liquid.

'Mufarah, the most prized drug of all, the drug of dreams. From the valley of the djinn. I obtained it for you, as I remembered our conversation in Kandahar and your interest in my country's traditions. It is for you to drink on retiring to bed.'

'Thank you, and how royal a thought.' Eagerly, I take the jar from him and put it on the table beside my chair.

As I do so, Assilan rises from his chair. Is now standing up. 'You must sleep now.'

I rise with him, and see him to the door.

His hand is in mine. A warm, dignified handshake our farewell.

I put the jar containing the mufarah, from the valley of the djinn, to my lips. Swallow it, in the hope of a wondrous dream.

# part two

*To you that delight in riddles,*
*that love the twilight,*
*whose soul is lured as by flutes to every labyrinth.*
*To you alone I tell this riddle that I saw...*
Nietzsche

## nineteen

A shrill peeping; my alarm clock. 7.30am. Reluctant wakefulness. A strange all-pervasive calm. Don't move, it seems to say. I lie still, held by an exquisite tranquillity.

But I have a plane to catch. Get up! I drag my body from the bed.

It feels leaden. As if it doesn't belong to me.

I shower, dress, tidy an oddly uninhabited self. Pick up my possessions. Somnambulistically step out into a taxi, to the airport.

It's clearly going to be a beautiful day.

The airport. I've completed the check-in formalities, and now I'm to go through a set of doors, carrying only my case of films. One of the desk officials is sending my camera case and suitcase through another door with my other luggage.

The place looks deserted. Am I the first passenger or the last?

Over there, to my right, one lonely customs officer is standing on the other side of a long, thin, knee-high aluminium inspection table.

I feel so tiny; he looks so tiny. This hall is so huge…

I walk across and stand facing him. I meet his eyes. They are not kindly.

He gestures to me to open my film case, picks up one of my films. Is putting it back, disinterested.

I wait.

Here comes my camera case, my suitcase. He's gesturing to me to open them. Is running his hands through my clothes. Now he turns his attention to my cameras. My wide-angle lens – he's looking through its wide eye the wrong way. Frowning.

'What were you doing in Afghanistan?' It sounds like a line in a play.

'I am a tourist.' My voice sounds quiet, almost asleep.

He's returned the lens to the case. Is slowly picking up my telephoto lens… camera bodies. My Leicaflex. My Hasselblad. Is running his fingers around the edges of my camera case. Now down the sides. His manner is cold and deliberate.

I know what he's doing, he's poking his way into me through my possessions. Look away, search the surrounding space.

The customs hall is vast, crudely built. Soundless.

Why am I the only one?

Where are the other passengers?

*Pe-eeeeeeep!* High, loud, *piercing.*

The customs officer is blowing his whistle!

My body, jellifying – a swarm of aggressive rattish faces rushing at me.

*I'm surrounded.*

A blur of rat teeth, tight excited black eyes. Hands, clutching my arms. Am I melting through the floor? They're propelling me toward a door.

On the other side more small, thin, rat-faced men are chattering feverishly, surrounding me.

'Sit!' A customs officer points to a bench.

I'm not alone. An extremely long-legged, neat blond man is sitting on the bench. His blue eyes blue-glide uncomfortably off mine. He looks embarrassed.

I *need* to sit.

We're sitting close.

Across the room, between the chaos, two customs officers are shouting simultaneously into a telephone receiver.

The palms of the blond man's hands are blackened – with dye? He sees me looking.

'Smuggling, hashish.'

I am agape. But he is so well dressed, meek! His accent is European.

Two unpleasant-looking European males are swaying into the room. They're both fat, with small eyes squinting pig-like from cheeks puffy with alcoholic excess. Grotesque twins, who stand with their legs apart and stare at the smuggler and me, while listening to a customs officer chatter effusively – about me, or the man next to me?

Their mean green pig-eyes are shifting onto me… onto the smuggler. Behind them the crowd of custom officers watches.

The twins are nodding their heads, muttering something to the man in charge.

They're leaving. As they do the crowd of officers collapses back into feverish excitement.

An officer approaches. 'Together, together.' He's bringing the palms of his hands together. Demonstrating? What?

An upward jerk of his left hand. He is ordering me to stand. Is pointing to a small room. I'm to go in? His eyes push me.

Inside, a little man grabs my hands, turns them flat, palms spread. Brusquely rubs my palms and fingers with ink. Black ink. He's rolling, printing them onto page after page of blank paper. I watch as blank paper fills with the secrets of my skin.

Perhaps it is because of the pressure being exerted on my hand, but I can feel myself awakening. I want to ask, 'What's happening?' Instead I look about me, searching for a face to reassure me that all is well.

A middle-aged, not unkindly-looking man with a moustache connects, comes up to me and introduces himself as the senior customs officer. He's calling me 'dear' – *pat, pat* – telling me that in half an hour I will be released.

Perhaps this is no more than a shadowy side-alley in an otherwise controllable dream after all. Perhaps I'm still asleep?

The little man has returned my hands to me, stained.

But my beloved companions – my cameras and film? Where are they?

A fatherly pat on my shoulder: 'Half an hour.'

Half an hour. What about my flight?

The senior customs officer wants to know more about my cameras. 'As these possessions are so cherished they must be *very expensive*?'

I flash back to the years it has taken me to acquire them – years of living on five dollars a week. 'Yes, they are very expensive,' I tell him.

## twenty

Half an hour, an hour.

They're ordering us to stand. Gosh, how tall and thin this smuggler is.

The customs officers surround us; take us (an unmistakable deep rush-roar, an aircraft taking off) upstairs, into a cafeteria.

'This table.' We sit.

In front of us is a large window to the airport and the landscape beyond.

Such a beautiful day, one of those rare and magical days where mountains stand clear and sharply white against a becalmed blue sky.

I already know the plane has gone without me. It has flown into that beautiful blue infinity. A feeling of bereavement sweeps through me.

I glance at the smuggler. His blue eyes stare forlornly into that unshackled space. He senses me, turns; a comfortless mirror.

The customs officers face us, watching us with undisguised glee. And drinking tea.

Ten, fifteen minutes. They are rising. Encircling us: black-cloud-crow-like. Taking us back down the stairs. Out to… *police vans?*

'Where are *my* cameras?' I shout.

I'm hustled into a van, handcuffed to a plump young policewoman. She is young but looks old; self-righteousness has worn its way into her features, giving her a lifeless, stupid look. I would photograph her if I had my cameras.

'Your parents will be sad for you.' She has turned the knife. An immediate and devastating realisation overwhelms me.

*Captured.*

Tears, unstoppable tears. The young policewoman all the while watching me with undisguised contempt.

I stare through the van window, crying uselessly.

My tears stop abruptly as a huge stone wall looms. We drive alongside it, through a set of tall gates. The van stops outside a large grey building. The policewoman releases me from the handcuffs.

Armed soldiers surround me.

*Frightened. Cold.*

I am taken into a filthy, sunless room. Icy. A chair, a desk, and several surly uniformed men.

The smuggler – a Dane – has arrived too.

We have to stand. Shivering.

Two or more hours pass.

*Numb.*

More soldiers have come in. Are now taking us into another building.

The room is larger, warmer, and is filled with heavily built men wearing black suits and white shirts. One points to us – to two thin chairs. We sit. Hard wooden chairs, blank walls.

The smuggler and I do not dare to speak.

They are talking to us in Afghan – it is absolutely incomprehensible. Smoking cigarettes. Running their knife-eyes over me – *black coals, black holes. Malevolence.*

The minutes tick their way into late afternoon. The hard chair is cutting off the circulation to my legs. I can no longer feel them.

Early evening. The smuggler is chain-smoking. The group of men are also chain-smoking; a crowd of mouths, sucking, blowing. White air mists my eyes. I look to the floor. Ash. Crushed butts, surrounding the smuggler's polished shoes.

I feel ill. Think I might be going to faint.

He's speaking, in English. The severe-faced man seated behind the desk. Am I fainting? He's saying: 'You are to go to the prison for *one night.*'

*Prison!*

The smuggler bounds to his feet in a surge of protest: loud, angry – demanding that he be allowed to make contact with his embassy. He's glancing at me, urging me to do the same. Why didn't we do this earlier?

There's no resistance; we're free to contact our embassies. Except my legs are dead. Pins and needles, and a feeling of overwhelming fatigue.

There is no representative for my distant homeland here. Only the British embassy. The smuggler finds this out for me, gives me a number. I stagger to my feet.

Thank goodness, an English-speaking voice – the British consul. I tell him my story; he tells me it is too late in the evening to do anything. He will investigate bail procedures in the morning.

I put the phone back on its cradle.

Alone, I am taken into yet another concrete room. Body stiff. Grey, silent. A peculiar painless emptiness.

Two soldiers, bearing rifles. They are beckoning to me, marching me into a small room. My suitcase – it's here. I'm to pick it up.

Two soldiers, two guns, one either side of me, marching me into… *darkness.*

One step, two steps, three… My heart is fluttering. Winging into a light, frantic beat. I am being escorted to *my death.* My own body taking me…

One step, two steps, three… only the sound of footsteps on gravel. A tiny beacon of light – torchlight – leads the way.

The soldiers have stopped.

In front of us, darker than this black black night, a heavy square: the prison door…

*Abyss…*

## twenty-one

A soft thud. The door closing behind me. I'm in a room, womb-like. As black as the cosmos.

Silence… a deep sigh: *I am alive.*

Music; a chorus of high-pitched female voices, arising from shadows and small stars of light… approaching: hands extended like tentacles, reaching, feeling their way toward me. Warmly gripping, leading me.

Across an open yard… I glance up at the night sky. And I perceive why the blackness of this night. The new moon has been in eclipse and now, sickle-thin and fragile, is emerging from her dark meeting with the sun, as I, held by the hands of women am led onwards… up some steps and through a doorless entrance into an ancient honeycomb of cells.

My new captors, excited, usher me toward a small room. I stop at its door, my eyes filled with the eyes of women sitting on a raised platform. Five-six women of varying ages and tribal types.

Astonishment! They're beautiful, in their laced-edged pantaloons reaching down to their feet, exquisitely embroidered dress-smocks covering their upper bodies, toenails and fingernails painted. Make-up, mascara and caste or tribal marks adorn their faces. In their eyes is a sensual, almost erotic aliveness. A veiled older woman is sitting in the shadows.

I take it all in within a second's flash. So so so *nervous.*

I'm close to the open doorway. To my right, another room. Harem curtains open – white soft – enclosing two extraordinary women, watching me. Without smile or blink. One is sitting cross-legged and pink-scarfed, her large silken red breasts spilling over shining crimson pantaloons. Masculine. Black caste mark on her forehead, heavily kohl-painted eyes powerfully boring into me, implacable, leonine. I blink. Shift my gaze. Onto the other; velvety plump, reclining in voluminous blue, a splash of cushions, black hair spilling out onto brilliant colours. Face soft, pampered, olive-white. Almond eyes – dark-sensual. Equally vigilant.

I turn away and enter the cell. The women are beckoning, reaching out their hands, eyes upon mine. Smiling. They want me to join them on the platform.

A space is cleared for me to sit and I am handed a glass of tea. A heavenly-hot-sweetness sinks into the parchment of my tongue. It is my first drink since partying with Assilan and his friends the night before.

I'm also drinking in the other prisoners. They are disarmingly childlike, wide-smiling, wide-eyed. My nervousness lessens – they seem so courteous and gracious. Not at all the hard, coarse and frightening criminals I would have imagined them to be.

A woman about my age, obviously less shy than the others, leans toward me, reaching her face close to mine.

'Your name?'

'Victoria.'

A chorus of *VictoRRiaas* echoes back.

Her hand is on her chest. 'Sediqua, my name. Little English, only me speak. I, your sister.' She's excited, definite, if not a touch superior in manner.

I'm suddenly *so tired*.

Sediqua, my 'sister', says something to a younger woman. The women shift positions, remaining cross-legged. A thin grass mat unrolls. Sediqua gestures to me to sleep.

Exhaustion overcomes me…

Someone's hand on my ankle, gently shaking it. I open my eyes.

She's dumpy, jovial, young and mischief-eyed. Sign-languaging to me to roll up my mat. To get up.

Where are the others, the five or more women who were here last night?

The girl is crouching on the narrow strip of floor alongside the platform, bending over a large pot of bubbling food on a small Primus stove. She has her back to me.

A pungent, nauseating smell of coriander and stewing goat meat permeates the air. I feel sick, possibly because I'm on my hands and knees, rolling up my mat.

Sediqua, my newly acquired sister, has returned. 'Come for wash.' Authoritatively organising me.

Wobbling, wobbling like a mechanical doll, following Sediqua out across a mud courtyard, through a walkway of grey stone walls, into another smaller courtyard.

Here, a hand-pumped well, with numerous rainbow-coloured women gathered around it. Children! Cooking pans, clay urns and clothes.

Water spills in spurts in rhythm with a rust-coloured metal arm, groaning metallically as a woman's strong hand grips and pumps. The women, children are all smiling – open mouths gawping, eyes glistening with amazement, curiosity.

Cupping my hands. Cold. As cold as a winter well's water can deeply be.

I splash my face, telling myself to try to wake up. Try to make sense of this – these colourful women, grey prison walls. Hallucination?

A sudden pain grips me. An *urgent* need to go to the lavatory. I clutch my stomach. 'Toilet.'

A determined, authoritative expression spreads across Sediqua's face. She quickly leads me back into the larger courtyard, a scramble of excited children following us.

She's pointing up some crumbling stone steps. Above those stone steps.

Hurriedly climbing the steps I step into what has to be one of the world's most revolting toilets: three holes punched into the elevated concrete floor, jellyish yellow-brown sewage quivering cauldronishly beneath them.

An unbelievable stench.

I have no choice. I crouch, hold my breath, press fingers against nostrils.

Don't look. Ignore these girls watching, giggling.

*Hold* my breath…

I rush from the toilet my chest bursting for oxygen. But the stink follows me like a piece of rotten meat tied to the ankle of the insane – a standard form of exorcism in parts of Asia.

Halfway across the mud courtyard, oxygen starved, I gasp the scent of three almond trees, their pink blossoms aburst.

My breath steadies. Thank God my 'one night' is over. I do not have to suffer such foul degradation again.

Recovering, I survey my environment. It's a basic oblong, divided into two square courtyards: this one and the one with the well. They are linked by an alley leading off from the concrete parapet rimming the eastern wall. The sand-mud courtyard in which

I'm standing is surrounded by doorless cells. Each cell has wooden shutters and glass windows, which open out to an elevated roofed-over stone and concrete veranda.

Hemp-rope and wood beds are scattered on the veranda, which appears to be a walkway and sleeping area. The prison is old, dilapidated, almost quaint. It is constructed of stone, mortar, brick, concrete.

Armed guards patrol the flat prison roof.

One is looking down at me; I retreat into the cell.

It is full of breakfasting women: slurping, chewing, swallowing a fat-thick soupy mixture of goat meat and rice. The smell is thick-sweet and fatty – nauseating. They want to share it with me. I politely refuse.

'Nan?' Sediqua offers me a pancake of unleavened bread instead, and a glass of steaming black tea loaded with – too late – a heaped tablespoon of white sugar.

The women make room for me to join them.

I tear the bread. Crisp-soft, with the taste of an earth oven flame. *Delicious.* I haven't eaten for thirty-six hours.

A crowd has gathered at the cell door and window; a host of hypnotised sapphire-black eyes are staring at me. Women's faces, all uncovered: dumbstruck, curious, shy, guileless. They're lovely.

A little shift in my being, a subtle settling of nerves. What refreshingly unthreatening faces. I realise that I've been lonely for the feminine; the open faces of 'sisters'. Until now I hadn't realised just how lonely.

The women, and girls, children and babies, their heads poking between bodies of cloth and veils, have a question. Sediqua is their voice: 'Why you here in prison?'

Why indeed?

'Mistake, today go.' My words are few and simple. But did she comprehend, and convey this to the crowd?

A subdued murmuring. A silent watching in their eyes. What are they thinking?

I have a question for Sediqua: 'Who are those two women in the next cell?'

'One in red, she Queen Candi. She number one. Other, she Marie.'

# twenty-two

It is Saturday. Visitors' day, according to Sediqua. I console myself with the knowledge that the consul will soon be here.

The crowd has now dispersed and, without entirely losing interest in the novelty of my presence, the remaining women are busying themselves. Nails are studiously repainted in various shades of pink and red. Long thick hair is replaited with ribbons, heavy layers of powdery kohl reapplied to the rims of their excited, preoccupied eyes. In anticipation of the arrival of their families?

One by one the painted ladies filter out into the warm spring day, fluttering across the mud courtyard, over to where a large collection of women have gathered. Only one, an unpainted, veiled woman, remains. She sits quietly in a corner. It is the older woman I'd glimpsed last night.

An atmosphere of impatience draws me out of the cell… into the courtyard… over to the prisoners' visiting area.

Here a hundred colourful bodies and intense yearning voices are shoutingtalkingshrieking – competing, squeezing, reaching to see…

A momentary parting of the wall of flesh gives me a glimpse of the visitors' room. It is the pitch-black room of last night. It's tiny – no more than six feet by five, with a door and a single, small, barred, glassless window, large enough for two or three faces only. Is this the prisoners' and visitors' viewing grate? And there, sitting in a corner opposite the grate, the heavy-set, leonine-eyed Queen Candi.

Just a peek before a squash of astonished faces and wild excitement close her to my view. I step back, out of the crush.

A separate door, a tall wooden gate adjoining the visitors' viewing area, is opening. A handful of older women come in and disappear into the cells. Mothers?

I cross back over the mud courtyard and sit on a bed.

The consul *will* come. He said he would.

Waiting and watching, I find myself slowly, slowly relaxing, calmed by this prison, its absence of threat. It's very strange, but the excited throng of women and children actually feels pleasant.

The armed guards on the roof don't look very threatening, or even interested. And over there, in a room close to that awful loo, a woman who looks as if she might be a policewoman and a gnarled-looking man who could be a clerk don't seem in the least interested in the prisoners.

A rush of exotic young women have spied me from the other side of the courtyard and are making a beeline for me… They're surrounding me, flashing their black eyes, excited. Flirting with me? They're overwhelmingly cheeky, curious.

Now they're fluttering away, back to the visitors' area.

Here they come again – unashamedly, gracefully sexual; embracing each other, teasing – yes, openly flirting. Is it excitement or anxiety? Women are highly sexed, I remember Assilan telling me. That is why they need to be protected. Is this why they're prisoners?

Fluttering away again.

It's puzzling. Who's in control here? Surely someone is keeping order among this mix? Perhaps Queen Candi *is* a queen. She looks omniscient enough – Queen of the Prison. A woman ruling women. In this male-dominated culture what a paradox that would be.

My imagination awakens: if Candi is a queen, then a subculture, a wholly different system must exist here. What about the Queen's companion, Marie? I haven't seen this voluptuously sensual woman among the crowd today. She must be, second in command?

Again, here they come, the *beauties*. Reels of colour surround me. Two, flinging themselves onto the bed on either side of me, place their arms about my shoulders. Erotic, burning black eyes peer into mine.

*Vic-tor-ia, Vic-tooor-ia!*

They know my name. Are shouting it – competing for my attention. Uninvited closeness, claustrophobia.

'Your name?' they coo.

They've just said it. I say it again. 'Victoria.'

'Vic-toor-ria!' Their rendition is high, musical. Not unpleasant-sounding.

But they're squeezing my arms too tightly. Pain and impatience shoot from my eyes, but to no effect. One has a deep scar running down her right cheek, wisps of black hair falling about her black eyes. An impressively husky 'I *lurve* you' falls from her mouth as I look at her.

'Thank you,' I reply, priggishly.

They tire of me. Rise up… are fluttering away… leaving me with the thought: how free in their feelings these beauties are, bold, imprisoned against their will.

Vague thoughts are interrupted by a chorus of echoing *Vic-toRR-iaas* summoning me.

Yes!

Eager, ready to leave, I squash my way through the crowd of women to the viewing grate.

'I am Andrew Winterbottom, the British consul.' He is short, not much taller than myself, nor much older. He is casually dressed, wearing an open-necked speckled shirt and brown jacket. It's the weekend.

British, to the point, and full of an impatient self-importance.

The crowd is loud and bothersome – I have to strain to hear his every word.

'Regrettably there is no chance of obtaining your release today as the chief prosecutor holding your file is not available. And as it is Easter Sunday tomorrow I'm afraid I won't be available. But I will attend your situation on Monday. So, until then.'

A 'chin-up' half-smile.

He's going, folding his way back through the crowd.

I walk back across the courtyard toward the hemp-rope bed. Sink into it.

Stunned.

So few words. Such a tiny moment in time. But what a hold – *ghastly authority* – over me.

At two o'clock visitors' day has finished, the prisoners' ration of uplifted emotion cut by the hand of a clock. No bell or call – simply a forlorn, straggling retreat.

Stillness. A void. Time marked by a yawn of shadows stealing silently across the courtyard.

A festering.

By late afternoon a cold chasm of gloom fills mind and space alike.

*Shriek!* By the visitors' room a clash of rainbows, snatching, tearing at each other. A fight has broken out between the two beauties who had been squeezing my arm and *lurving* me earlier in the day.

A siren? The other women pour out of their cells and suddenly the mud courtyard is aswirl with hysterical women, the sounds of inconsolable despair, bodies flaying, cavorting in a weird wailing battle.

A blur of red leaps out from a recess, charging along the concrete parapet, halts a small distance above the distraught women.

*Snap!*

A wide leather whip cracks over the women's heads. Immediate hush. Queen Candi glowers, her whip held at arm's length. Utterly fierce. She moves down the steps toward the women, who have begun to weep, wail, plead with their number one. She's merging with the women – listening to them.

Sigh. The tension has defused, the unruly are ruled.

Day is drifting into another night…

## twenty-three

My feet are moving. A hand is on my ankle… it is the round, cheerful girl waking me again.

Now *pain*, shooting through my gut. My stomach's puffed, gurgling… The hellhole. I rush over to it… holding my jersey over my nose and mouth as I enter. I find my way to the well and splash myself. I greet the faces staring at me.

Back in the cell Sediqua and the other women are slurping their revolting breakfast with an air of heavy resignation. There is a glass of sweet black tea for me. I take it out to the mud courtyard. Sit on a hemp-rope bed.

Today is Sunday, Easter Sunday. A splash of spilt tea looks like chocolate. Chocolate, *hot* chocolate. *Easter eggs* – pink and white marshmallow-centred chocolate-coated Easter eggs.

*Home.* How I ache to be there, naked in my own spacious, deliciously warm and cosy bed. Eating an Easter egg. I shall have to dream.

A glance to my left, to a single hemp-rope bed positioned about twelve feet away. Lying on it are Queen Candi and Marie, *squashed* together, holding, hugging each other. They look like a large red and blue two-headed person. Now they languorously arise and begin to stroll arm in arm around their palace grounds.

The morning is quiet. The women are subdued, preoccupied with repairing the previous day's damage to each other, their garments. I see-sense their grief. Their mutual forgiveness.

What can I do but sit… outside on the hemp-rope bed, which seems to have become my spot.

Children, coming toward me, stopping-standing an arm's length away. Five little eye-darting girls in miniature dress-smocks and pantaloons. Fingers to their chins, cheeks. Coiling and squirming with excitement, curiosity and a knotted-haired gypsy-nomad-village-children's cheekiness. Running away. Looking back at me.

Here come the beauties, wrapping their arms about me, bending seductively, cheekily, face-close.

Sediqua and the jovial one are sitting either side of me in sisterly support. They feel for me. And they must know how it feels: to become a self divided: all freedom of choice, freedom to be – lost. Or do they?

Remorse soaks through me like a thick bog – a thick parasite-infested bog. I have idiotically beheaded myself. How? Oh, if only I had obeyed my inner voice – that *tranquillity* on the morning of my flight three days ago. If only I had stayed in bed.

Still. Be still, I tell myself. There *will be* a way out of here.

Today Christ rises. Easter Sunday. Then Friday, the day of my arrest, was Good Friday, the day of Christ's crucifixion. The day of martyrdom and redemption.

Enclosed space, flesh trapped.

Queen Candi is coming toward me. She's accompanied by a Westernish-looking girl of about nineteen: thin, brown-red hair and dressed like a traditional Muslim woman. The Queen is smile-gesturing to me to talk with her.

Timidity and paranoia emanate from her staring eyes. Is she physically unwell, or merely damned?

'My name Victoria. English. You speak?'

A peculiar grimace-smile spreads across her face; unknowing. 'Poland. Husband Afghanistan. Him me imprison. Boyfriend.' She's holding four fingers in the air to indicate – her sentence? Four months or four years?

Shudder. There is a deadness in her eyes; she is lost to the knowing of self; raped – is she a mirror of my fate?

The Queen sees my discomfort, and, recognising our foreignness to each other, leads the girl away.

I'm disturbed. Was the Queen trying to warn me? Or she did she really think I could speak to this girl?

Queen Candi re-emerges from the alleyway alone. She walks along the concrete parapet on the opposite side of the courtyard toward the cells. That face and physique – she could be a mythic being. Anyway, a formidably strong woman, a fighter, the archetypal female warrior – a *lioness!* She turns upon my thought, glances across the courtyard at me, our eyes connecting across the distance.

A silver light plays upon my ring.

## twenty-four

Some hours later a chorus of *Vic-toRR-iaas* call-sing across the courtyard. I'm to go to the prisoners' viewing grate…

A soldier! The door is opened. The soldier leads me along the crunching gravel path I walked on that first night. Where is he taking me? Back to the building the smuggler and I sat in for so many hours? He leaves me at the door, gestures to me to go in.

The short walk from the prison has lifted my spirits and hope is high as I step into the room.

The vampirish men from the day of my arrest are there again. Pointing to me to sit on the same hard wooden chair.

I meet their gaze, levelly. Out of politeness.

A malevolence stares back at me – one woman, alone in a room full of male black eyes. The atmosphere is taut, thick-thin with nastiness.

I begin to lose my nerve… I stand. A mistake? I'm feeling terribly exposed. But it's too late: I hear myself addressing them, feel a smile spreading across my mouth. 'There has been an unfortunate error.'

The room contracts. Four walls; cold menace. A whiplash of anger, and a whining nasal voice demanding: 'What were you doing in Afghanistan?'

'Taking photographs. Marketplaces, goats, trees, village people. Only tourist shots,' I say earnestly.

'Where have you travelled?'

'I…'

'What hotels have you stayed in?'

'I…'

'Who do you know?'

He won't let me speak. I look around the room, at their faces, tight and sour with loathing.

Ten minutes, half an hour later – I have no idea – I am taken out, taken back.

I am disorientated, pass the hours in a brooding entrapment, into night, into sleep. Morning. I chew a piece of nan, drink a glass of hot tea. Strange pains shiver through my stomach, my guts.

The wall – I need to lean against it, stay still, stay close to the women – their shifting colours and sounds – a sing-song of voices murmuring around me, *silken-gliding*, blanketing the pain.

11am. The women check on me; small glances, quiet smiles… a little song from one of the peasant girls.

I'm not feeling well.

1pm, again the chorus: *Vic-toooor-ia…*

'Visitor.' Sediqua's eyes signal me to hurry.

It's the British consul, 'Andrew', peering officiously at me through the four greasy iron bars. He has just met the chief prosecutor.

In my language-starved state his round-vowelled words feel like giant meteorites hitting me.

'You have been charged with co-conspiring with a Danish national to smuggle hashish. Bail procedures will have to be investigated.'

My heart is galloping, my mind contracted in split-second-panic-guilt-flight-escape.

'But yesterday the men – the prosecutors – didn't give any indication of my being charged with smuggling. They only questioned me about where I'd travelled, what I had photographed, who I know!' My voice betrays my fear, confusion.

The consul's officious expression is unchanged. 'I have been informed by the prosecutors who interviewed you that three and a half kilos of hashish were found in your cameras.'

*Am I a smuggler with a memory blank? Did I compromise my freedom for my art, my art for my freedom?*

'My cameras! There was no hashish in my cameras. It's a physical impossibility. It's a lie,' I stare the consul defiantly in the eye. 'And I don't know this Danish man from Adam. I have never seen him before.'

A brief look of sympathy on the consul's face, a sense of 'reserved' understanding.

'Can you get me out of here?' I beseech him, humiliated by my dependence on him. His stuffy superiority.

'We must follow the necessary procedures if [*if?*] you're to obtain bail or be released,' he replies coolly. He will, however, speak to the Governor of Kabul, to seek his assistance.

I'm in *serious* difficulties.

'I need food,' I tell him. 'I can't eat the prisoners' food. And my cameras. I *cannot* lose them. There was *no* hashish in them.' There's a tone of the panic-stricken mother in my voice.

His rose-pink face remains unmoved. He's become impatient. 'I will notify you of any developments as soon as possible.' He turns away abruptly.

Suddenly weak, I return across the mud courtyard holding on to his final sentence. *As soon as possible.* It is all I have.

## twenty-five

Easter Monday: the discovery of Christ's empty tomb. He, God-force, took his body with him. Smart move.

Unzzziiippping my suitcase. Inside, a rumpled disarray: a few tops-underwear-sarong-dresses, Assilan's stockings. A pair of light, loose, string-tied pants. Sandshoes. Sandals.

Trinkets – gifts: an engraved silver scroll-holder (a prayer inside?); a twin-faced silver horse, faces in profile; a necklace; a white marble oil burner shaped into the face of a sleeping sheep; an engraved mythological creature in bronze. Mr John's present.

Travel documents but no passport.

A triple-nibbed biro. Socks. Cosmetic bag: toothbrush, toothpaste – no shampoo, comb, no soap, neither my face soap nor my bar of Sunlight soap for washing my clothes. They've been stolen.

I haven't cleaned my teeth, brushed my hair or changed my clothes for three days.

The women are chatting among themselves.

My diary! They didn't take it. It opens to this page, this line:

*I'm a wanderer, wild and free, no solid walls imprison me.*

My chest swells. Tears are forming, rolling discreetly out of the corners of my eyes. Cutting hot little paths down my cheeks.

Sediqua turns her head, peers at me, my tears. She's leaning close, staring at me questioningly.

'No be sad. No cry.' Her voice is cross-serious, motherly.

'I'm thinking,' I reply.

'Thinking no good. No think. I Sediqua, I your sister, you *obey* me!'

I do obey her. Become numb.

Ten minutes later I notice that Sediqua has gone quiet, has tucked herself into a shadow. I peer into it.

What is this – Sediqua crying? Her head has dropped and she *is* crying, a long flow of real tears. I lean toward her.

'Thinking no good. No think. I Victoria, I your sister, you *obey* me!'

Gulps and sniffles. A sob. 'I not see my children for two and half years.'

'Why?'

'Husband me imprison, seven years: I love others mans.'

Seven years, she tells me, is the average sentence for female adulterers.

I look around at the other women in the cell, at the older woman in her corner. She's about sixty, thin and silent. A white net veil covers her head as she sits with her hand half-folded over the corner of her mouth, staring wistfully into inner space.

She looks over at me. Smiles forlornly, moth-gently.

Sitting cross-legged close to her, also veiled, is Marjohn. She is about twenty-two years old, plump and bejewelled. In her eyes I see the grief of another mother who's lost her children. Marjohn is plaiting the hair of a visiting beauty – a thick, rich mane. This girl is younger and carries a different pain.

The two dumpy adolescent girls who share the cell are at this moment squatting on the floor, tidying away plates and food. The jovial one is singing. They are always quick to laugh, and seem to enjoy their homely tasks: cooking, cleaning, serving. But they too are scarred; it shows in their bodies.

Sediqua has recovered some of her usual composure. I ask her about the others.

'Some stealing, some prostitution, some – most – for having boyfriend, adultery. Some, no crime, husband lie, no want wife. Husband family keep children, sometimes. I not see my children, ever maybe.'

'Same,' she gestures to the other women in our cell.

'You say: you marry man then he not love you, he put you in prison?'

Sediqua, with her bits and pieces of words, explains the marital laws of her people. I find that women, and men, have no right to choose their marriage partners. It is all organised by their parents. Neither of the betrothed is allowed to touch or speak to the other before their wedding, and often have no idea what their future spouse even looks like.

'Sometimes mans buy three, four wives, if he have money to pay; mans much money he sometimes buy girl. *No good* this mans. Make girl sick. Sometimes die.'

'No husband, children – woman nobody in Muslim law. Only mans important. Woman stay in house, husband, brother see her, not other mans. She whore if other mans see her. Then family no want her. She go to prison – here. Or, sometimes she killed, by husband, and husband family. By stone.'

She wants to know that I understand.

'Always this way?'

'In old days only important woman cover up. Special. Muhammad's wifes special. Arab. Now all womans do it. Law. Except modern womans in Kabul. Them education, same you.'

A mix of admiration and deference threads its way across Sediqua's features; to be educated and 'modern' is obviously her aspiration. And perhaps also her sorrow. Suddenly she switches off, turning back to the others.

I can't understand, can't comprehend let alone condone a law that sees a woman as having no value beyond that of property. Such lovelessness. But what it does explain is why I can neither sense nor see evil in these women.

The darkness speaks in deep breaths, inhaling-exhaling; my stigmatised cellmates, inches away, mercifully lost in sleep.

My mind won't rest. I need to make sense of where I am – this culture, to write it on the pages of my mind as if it were my diary.

*Finally, I understand why most of the men I encountered on my travels reacted to me as an object to be leered at and hunted. Not only must I have – face uncovered – appeared naked in their eyes, I was alone, accessible.*

*Am I – are we – just flesh, without spirit in this male culture? Is woman, to this God-male mind, a temptress to be punished with blindness, her 'highly-sexed' lowness to be hidden, forbidden? And is it only to other men that a man looks for his mirror-self, God-self?*

'Arrrrrrrr!'

A primeval roar descending through the night upon this thought. It's deep-throated, masculine. And coming from directly above my head!

'Arrrrrrrr!' The same sound echoes back from the other side of the courtyard.

'Arrrrrrrr!' This time quieter, further away. From somewhere beyond the prison.

The soldiers – it's the soldiers on the prison's rooftop, *roaring* to each other. Signalling? I'm fascinated.

'Arrrrrrrr!' 'Arrrrrrrr!' 'Arrrrrrrr!'

Half an hour later, another series of roars.

Half an hour later, another series of roars.

Half an hour later…

## twenty-six

Daybreak, day four, eyes closed, drowsily listening to the women stirring; soft sounds of cloth and limbs. It's soothing, allows me to know them without being known.

I recall my conversation with Sediqua the night before.

Eyes opened. I'm ashamed at how I've behaved among them – how broody and self-absorbed I've been. A few days for me but seven years for them, whose crime is no crime.

Sit up, and make amends for your insensitivity, I resolve.

A sharp-heavy pain in the region of my liver.

The punishment of the hellhole over once more I head toward the well where a group of women, squatting like kangaroos around a drain, are washing their clothes. An opportunity to demonstrate my new-found sisterhood. I stop by them, watch them a while, then ask their names. Exotic-symphonic sounds greet my ears in return.

They know 'Victoria', are playing with it, tossing it back and forth in a musical game. Smiling, they tease me with their lightening eyes.

A group of women are performing their morning ritual of filling their urns. My hair feels filthy. A handsome and strong-bodied peasant girl is holding the well handle. I gesture to her: 'Will you pump the icy water over my head?' She obliges, almost gleefully.

*Freezing* freshness.

Ripples of laughter from the women.

Shake-shaking my head, *splashes,* white teeth smiling… laughter. Laughing with them. At myself. Now finger-combing my hair, a feeling of my stolen wildness momentarily returning as I do.

Sediqua's hand, possessively gripping my triple-nib biro, presses down, carving a little blue person riding a surf ski: the Pashto equivalent of an 's'.

She sits next to me on the bed, teaching me her alphabet. She has surprised me; is literate in the Pashtun *and* the Roman alphabets. She is, she had proudly boasted, the only literate one of the hundred or so women here.

Next, a crescent moon with a small 'u' and a runaway tail: 't'. An upside-down figure 2 with a dot on top: 'k'. Another crescent moon, a dot where a chin would be: 'b'. 'S' is similar but a little different. And so on, the letters, to the spellbound gathering of young and old, fixing themselves to the paper through Sediqua's careful hand.

Next, pronunciation.

'Thh… a… guushh… tar.' Sediqua's rich throaty song of sounds is a word? She points to my silver sphinx ring. 'Thh… a… guushh… tar. You say.'

Plumping up my throat. A baby exotic bird warble gushes out.

Deep belly laughing, waterfalls of giggling from the crowd of women and children.

Sediqua tries again. 'Thhrr… a… guushhhtarrrr.'

I listen intently to her various inflections. Just one 'large' word.

An expectant hush. Sediqua stares at me sternly.

*How* can I reach down that far in my throat and *roll* up that sound? I suck back air and a sound triple flips over my tongue; hitting the roof of my mouth, cheekily leaps out.

This time I'm laughing too, belly laughing – tears and snorts and all…

Sediqua is not impressed. Her lips are tight. Learning is a serious business and inadvertently I've offended her. She's impatient and, judging by her expression, thinks I'm stupid.

She gives up – is she in a huff? – and returns to our cell.

I leave her be for a while. Then approach.

'Please, you draw me a picture?'

She is still cross with me, but the open, blank page of my precious diary is too great a temptation. She draws a butterfly. Two halves of a heart divided by a flame. The heart is upside down. The letter 's' is in the centre.

An eye, long lashes, heavy eyebrow and a wide-open O with a black • in the middle.

It is afternoon. A small radio murmurs in a corner of the cell. The women are discussing their large, masculine wristwatches. I know this because they are admiring them, the small variations in design.

They're eating again.

Now shifting around.

Some thread beads, sharing beads, comparing colour arrangements and each other's designs. Voices murmur, river-like.

Absorbed.

Outside, on the hemp-rope bed. I observe a little group of teenagers crouching on the stone steps outside the cell. They're smoking cigarettes, combing and picking through each other's hair.

Women drift through the passageway to the well area; children hang about, examining unseen things in one another's hands.

I look at my own feminine wristwatch. Three minutes past four. My gaze shifts onto my ring. In the 'stillness' of its inscrutable image I recall a fragment of my favourite poem, 'Beauty', by Baudelaire:

> *I am fair, O humankind, a reverie of stone!*
> *Upon my breast all mortal men have bruised themselves in turn,*
> *For it is made to fire poets' adoration…*
> *Silent as stone; lasting like stone…*
> *for centuries to come…*

I go back inside and doodle in my diary. Circles,
   circles
   swoo

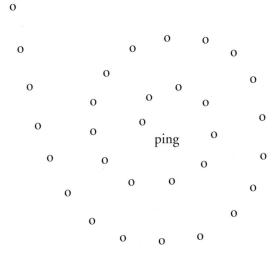

In time there is eternity.

# twenty-seven

Night has fallen on my fifth day in prison. I am lying sandwiched between the women in my cell.

Up until now I haven't minded being plonk in the middle of the platform, between Marjohn and Sediqua. I had reasoned that any bedbugs and other hell-borne night creatures creeping down the walls would sink their disease-bearing beaks into the first flesh they crawled on. If they did eventually find my body, they would be too blood-bloated to be bothered.

But tonight I'm flanked by the jovial 'prison maids' and I think I'm going to lose my sanity. The novelty of their sleeping arrangements has drawn them in so tight that their breathing sounds like two hurricanes doing battle through my ears. The one on my left, to add flavour to this windy-snorty carry-on, also happens to be chewing gum. *Chomp. Grind. Slobber.*

*Pop!* She's blowing bubbles.

*Pop!* Eyelashes away from my cheek, chewing.

*Pop!* I want to shout, 'Shut Up!' Do so in my mind.

Christianly, I 'turn the other cheek', only to find that I'm lying nose to nose with the shadowy pits of a pockmarked face. Her mouth is hanging open, releasing a putrescence of rotted food and tooth decay. I can see tiny lights in the pits of her eyes. She's staring at me.

I am forced to lie on my back, but I can't, have never been able to sleep on my back.

One-two-three hours… exhausted, rigid with tension, I begin to feel a *dangerous* anger. A soundless *scream* is tearing my chest. I *have* to get out of here.

I pray, as I prayed to my childhood God. In whispers… *let me out of here…*

The soldiers are beginning to roar.

One,

two,

three,

four, *five* roars, the last one different – quite muffled and sick sounding, like an animal being tortured.

'AaaaaahhhhhH!' There it is again. Again and again, knife-deep, agonised. Human.

How very small the soldiers' roars compared with the sounds of this unknown soul, hour upon hour upon hour bellowing forth its *pain*.

All through the night I am lacerated by this anguished cry, until it dies with the dawn.

## twenty-eight

Day. Praying with true desperation: Dear God – the merciful, the compassionate, everlasting refuge, *please* let me out of this prison, out of here… Dear God… please please *please* let me out… Dear…

A call!

Four faces are peering glassily at me through the grate; hippies – a male and three beaded girls, bearing that disconnected intensity of religious zealots. Children of God, they tell me.

The answer to my prayer?

*'We Love You, Love You, Love You.'* They're almost chanting. Americans. How did they know I'm in here?

No, one is from 'Orstraalia'. The British consul must have sent her. She has a 'groupie' type of face – transparent, eagerly familiar.

'We have brought you some food,' she says.

Food!

A brown paper bag is passed through the iron bars. A soft grunt sounds from behind me, from the keeper of the gate – Queen Candi – who is sitting impassively in her visitor-monitoring spot, wanting to inspect the package.

She hands it back to me. Four eggs, three tomatoes, a couple of handfuls of rice and a small withered *apple*. I can't fight the tears. It's homesickness, a deep longing.

The Children of Vapour are clearly concerned.

'Have you anyone who loves you? We love you. Where do you live? Do you have any messages, a place to stay when you are released? We have a room. Any letters you want us to post? God loves you.'

I have written a letter advising a friend of my predicament, just so someone will be aware of what has happened. I hand it to the Australian, and immediately feel it will never reach its intended destination.

Walking back across the mud courtyard I reach into the paper bag for the apple. One eager bite and I've cut it in half. Chewing, spitting it out. Bitter.

I keep some of the eggs and rice for breakfast the next morning: every suck, chew, swallow as intensely *delicious* as that of the previous day's boil-up.

Only two tomatoes remain. How can I get more?

Sediqua is all-knowing. 'You have buy food. Soldiers, soldiers go bazaar' – she counts on her fingers – 'four days. You not here then, maybe.' How sweetly she said this.

She's an odd sister, or maybe just a typical big sister, as all her information is measured. I must ask if I want to know anything as she doesn't often volunteer information. And in the last two days she's shown a reluctance to communicate in English, which I can understand; I can't even speak *one* word of her language.

But I also sense that Sediqua likes to exercise power by giving a titbit of insight, then switching off in mid-air. Just as she's caught my interest, she'll turn away and fall into conversation with the other women. Leaving me – deliberately? – forgotten. It's a kind of meanness that's at odds with the prison's communality. But then Sediqua is different from the other women. More modern. And, after all, my only 'voice' into the understanding of prison life.

'Prisoners pay money for place in cells.' She startles me: a new, unsolicited piece of information. I seize the opportunity. 'How you pay?'

'Sew clothes, embroidery, bead necklace, give soldiers, them take… sell bazaar. Job in prison, girls no money clean, cook. Sometimes family help.' She stares me in the eye, says emphatically: 'Prison not free!' And moves away from me. What is she trying to tell me?

*Diary:*
*Beads, round beads, long beads, glass beads, plastic beads, red beads, blue beads, white beads, yellow beads, green beads, black beads, thousands of tiny beads.*
 *Quick fingers needle pick-picking, thread-threading. A quiet chatter.*
 *The beads; the bazaar; my purchase, the cascading necklace: was it made by the*

*hands of my fellow prisoners? Should I take it from my suitcase, show it? Link it around*
*my neck, link with these women threading their imprisoned time?*
　　*No.*

My biro has three nibs: red, black, blue. One colour upon the other. Like a bruise.
Circles circle-swooping. They relieve the claustrophobia. Let me slip away into…

　　*…circles within the square, within the circle. Quadratura circulus – the squaring of the*
*circle. The symbol of wholeness, according to the alchemists of old…*

　　*'All straightness is a lie,' muttered the dwarf contemptuously. 'All truth is crooked and time*
*itself is a circle…'*

　　…thoughtlessness…

twenty-nine

Day six. Am feeling oddly sane. I must write.

　　*Diary:*
*A prisoner's observations of the prison life. Kabul Prison, Afghanistan, 1978. As gleaned*
*from watching the goings-on in my cell, the mud courtyard, the walkway and the well,*
*and Queen Candi and Marie's cell, which I have to pass by every time I enter or exit*
*the one I'm in. To these eyes the most interesting prison aesthetic is the Queen's and her*
*beloved's boudoir.*

　　*Most often a heavy curtain of cloth or a white semi-transparent muslin netting is*
*drawn across their door, closing or screening them off from the prison world. Every*
*morning the curtains are tied back, indicating that one or more of the prison maids is*
*in there, attending to the domestic needs of Queen Candi and Marie: clearing away*
*dishes, sweeping the floor, tidying their bed.*

　　*Occasionally I get a peek, a misty view of Marie reclining among a beautiful bouquet*
*of cloth and patchwork, a mother from one of the other cells combing her cosmos of*
*black hair or cleansing it with scented oils.*

　　*Although I know that every prisoner (bar myself) has to pay for their imprisonment,*
*the women's social structure is based on a system that is independent of external authority.*

A sort of imprisoned 'self-sufficiency' allows the prisoners – composed of various tribal types – to live together democratically.

On top, 'number one', Queen Candi, works three worlds: firstly, seeing to the peace and needs of her 'family', secondly, liaising with soldiers and authorities. Thirdly, for the rest of the time, closed in an embrace with her beloved. Like Baudelaire's 'Cats': 'They dream and take the noble attitude of sphinxes lazing in deep solitudes... which seem to slumber in an endless dream...'

Marie is the Queen's consort, her jewel. She reminds me of a plump Persian palace cat, her passionate black eyes gazing with a languid hauteur and grace as she reclines in sated comfort. Sometimes she arises from her cushions to call a small boy, who doesn't ever reply.

The 'mothers' range in age from their mid-teens to late sixties. Some have their children here with them, but the ones in my cell are alone, quiet. They are the sewers, the bead-threaders, the carers: plaiting hair, painting nails, pandering to the beauties' trapped-wild energy. Massaging them, one another.

The 'beauties' are flirtatious, loud and filled with tease and scattiness. They're the prison's eyes, watching, ever seeking connection through their hands, bodies, tongues. Tactile not tactful.

The 'prison maids' are peasants with strong arms and asexual bodies. The two in my cell are always busy (bar an occasional brooding cigarette on the steps) cooking, cleaning, washing, singing.

Little girls imitate the chores of their mothers; the boys run hither and thither, appearing, disappearing, exuberant. Babies contentedly cradle upon their mothers, or crawl about in search of dirt and discovery.

A great big family of women and children. A matriarchy.

Then there's me, the prisoners' 'guest', a foreigner with disintegrating health and an increasingly short temper. My life held in abeyance.

Silence, speechlessness – it opens the self to more subtle and communicable languages: the languages of gesture, of expression, of being – the universal communication. This is how the women protect their peace, their communal harmony. But the silence never lasts long; they hold each other together with their tongues, talkingtalking.

*I have no speech to bind me to another. But for my basic humanity I am without relationship to this world.*

Watching, doodling in my diary. The circles now have an eye.

# thirty

*Diary:*
*TIME: how to know – as do the blind – to be still within it; and not so filled with hunger, emptiness. The body in its boredom, the heart in its loneliness, seeking, seeking. The manner of mothers bereft of their babies, eating, eating; and in fat-folds of grief, sinking.*

My seventh day as a prisoner; the afternoon. The worst time. A thick emptiness fills the air; the eating is over and the women – those in my cell and, I assume, the other prisoners – are withdrawn into a sort of digestive melancholia.

Shifting, sitting outside on the hemp-rope bed close to my cell.

Close by, squatting on the steps leading onto the veranda, the pock-faced prison maid smokes a cigarette. And studies me.

The policewoman and her clerk have locked their office and gone for the day. Two o'clock is office closing time – after almost a week I have worked this out.

Time drifts.

Children are scattered around the courtyard.

Women wander, back and forth.

Inward.

Staring at the earth.

*Waiting.*

All of a sudden a little hand darts between me and the mud-grey and touches my knee. I look up. A handsome little boy is before me, staring at me unwaveringly. He taps my knee again… staring cheekily – is challenging me to play, to 'chase him'. I'm weak, stomach-bloated, starved…

But I jump up… *Charge…* he runs…

Suddenly: movement everywhere. Toddlers and children, the prison maids, *hurtling* around the open areas: chased, chasing, *Shrieks, Squeals… across* the courtyard, *up* the steps to the parapet, *along* the eastern wall, *around* the veranda to the cells, *down* the steps outside my cell, *back* along the courtyard…

*Touch* a child – excited shriek. Touch another, another, others, tumbling squealing thrilled.

Puffing; I am breathless with chase. Have to stop.

As I catch my breath Sediqua emerges from the cell, stretches her arms above her head. The fun and games have raised her and she joins me.

The children crowd about, jostling and giggling.

'Who's that boy?' I ask Sediqua, curious to know about the handsome little game initiator.

'He prison spy, he climb hole in wall and see soldiers bring you.' So that is how the women knew to come and find me, to lead me that first night, the night of the eclipse. 'He Marie's son, his name Muhammad.' Sediqua is obviously in a relaxed mood, and I have an opening.

'What crime Queen Candi and Marie?' I casually, carefully, ask.

'Queen, murder; Marie, adultery,' she equally casually replies.

The children are staring at me, all wild and wired with chase. But little Muhammad is no longer among them.

## thirty-one

Saturday. It is visitors' day again.

The British consul is dapper and confident. I'm to meet the prosecutors this morning. Now.

The prison door opens. I walk through, spring released, thinking that his demeanour heralds a breakthrough. I realise otherwise as soon as I am beyond the prison door.

Waiting just past the throng of visitors are two *very* clean Western women. The consul introduces me to his girlfriend and her mother. They smile at me with a mix of uncertainty and sympathy. I've not seen 'my own kind' for what feels like a hundred years and the yearning to talk to them is almost overwhelming. I force myself to stifle it – not appropriate.

As we walk together to the prosecutors' office I feel self-conscious about my decaying appearance. They're so primly English. I keep my head down, quietly pained at the way the two women glide in their mid-heeled expensive shoes.

The consul, as if to deepen my humiliation, instructs me on how to behave before the prosecutors.

'Keep your eyes lowered.' If I stared any lower I'd be on my hands and knees.

'Don't speak unnecessarily. Sit in a reserved fashion and *please* don't ask questions. I will do that.' Does he think he's speaking to a backward child? I feel like a backward child; I've been locked away for over a week – eternity.

I walk through the door alone… stiffen… I'm to stand at the back of the room. The chairs have gone.

They don't question me at all. Just sit and stare at me. It's a form of torture.

In the tense silence I picture the consul and the women outside – *just through the door, down the steps, on the grey-white flat sand. Her pearl-white shoes; polished. And hers, pale blue, round-toed… protected.* The thought prevents me from breaking into little pieces; the prosecutors' faces, the atmosphere, are so stony – *cruel.*

I'm out. Inwardly shaking. And standing close to the two women, who attempt to mask their awkwardness by telling me they're 'on holiday'. I feel like crying.

Five minutes later the consul reappears, looking as if he's been spat at; stern and piqued. And to the point. 'I'm afraid to say that the prosecutors regard you as unclean – your character, that is. Consequently they are resistant to your release.' His jaw protrudes and the skin between mouth and chin is puckered. He presses his lips manfully, Britishly, tight.

I'm belittled beyond measure, yet I manage to squeak: 'I'm not well.' In some peculiar way I think that my words will feed through the consul's head into those of the bullies in the office. That they will look upon me with mercy.

'Well, considering your circumstances this is only to be expected,' the consul's glib reply.

The two women look at me with genuine pity. I can see it in their powdered faces, in their eyes: 'A tragedy.' Self-pity wells in me.

Dirty-stinking-*privateless*-prison. Anger, humiliation, locking me in. In the cell.

Stare-staring at the fluidity of Islamic script, swirling, *night-black upon the gold.*

Framed.
Hanging upon the wall.

*Diary*
*Good Friday, Christ died and the new moon went into eclipse over India and*
*Afghanistan, heralding the Islamic New Year. I became a prisoner and something went*
*from me. Ambition. Something new appeared: the faces of women, imprisoned. Sinking*
*Down*
*Down*

From her viewing-room corner throne Queen Candi has seen me coming back into the prison. Has seen my state of mind. Perhaps my desolation has inspired her sympathy.

It's evening, dark. The eating is finished for the day and something out of the ordinary is happening.

The women are tidying up, clearing the platform, pulling out the tin trunks they store underneath. They flit in and out of the cell, a hushed excitement, an almost conspiratorial air about them.

Queen Candi, choosing a moment when all but the older mothers are outside, slips into my cell. She's holding a smoking, ember-red cigarette – hashish, I can smell it. Her eyes are fixed on mine, *urging* me to smoke. Then, amid frantic attempts to disperse the clouds of smoke by fanning her hand across my face, she leaves again.

A circle moon ascends the night sky as a single drumbeat repeats its way across the courtyard. Laughter. The sound of feet.

Women adorned in a passion of colour and vibrancy filter into the cell carrying hand drums, rattles, a cassette player.

Marjohn, the epitome of womanly warmth and gentleness, gestures to me to sit on a cushion in the corner. The cell fills with an exuberance of chatter, *excitement…*

All at once the drum beats, hand drums shake, the cassette tape jumps – electric wailing, the women singing and clapping their hands in lively unison.

Is that the dumpy nocturnal gum-chewing maid who is taking the makeshift stage? Her face is transformed by exotic make-up, eyes ablaze – I almost don't recognise her in her emerald green and shivers of silver dress, a centre star upon her brow, plaited ribbons streaming from her hair, ankle bells, half-painted toes.

Dancing, delicate, sinuous. Light-fiercely toe-drumming the platform boards. Whirling, twisting, turning, her palms facing out, now in. Smiling, her eyes on mine.

Now the other prison maid, another, and others from neighbouring cells, each following and repeating – to the sounds of drums, feet, music – the magic of the first.

The mothers' turn. Marjohn, her eyes kohl-painted in orbits of black, dressed in a divine swirl of purple, goddess-smiling eyes to mine. Blue, white, black, greens, some lightly veiled, as if within dreams: one by one the mothers weave their sensual spell, smilingsmiling, dancingdancing into my eyes.

The air is hot and heavy with the smell of lotus oil and perfumes. The cell is asizzle with women, sensuality, vibrant eyes – a crowd of moist warm breath caressing every sense.

The beauties shimmer in, dark-flashing-eyed. As cobras, rise, high, hood-wide and bold… Faster, faster their serpent weave – smooth necks sliding, enticing, striking, inflaming, enfolding me and one another.

Amrita to the deities, essence of immortality.

I am sitting on a cushion in a corner of a prison cell in Afghanistan. Mesmerised. An initiate disrobed of her ego, being inducted into a secret cult. These are high priestesses, not prisoners. Now I see them.

Queen Candi and Marie enter, dressed in moon goddess Red, every regal and imaginable sexual shade of it; from head to lip, breast to buttock, fingertip to toenail.

Sphinx-eyed, their dance of love begins slowly, heavily: a rhythmic beat-drumming of their toes upon the shaking floor. Beat-drumming their toes as they hold only to each other's eyes. Not mine.

The music intensifies, faster, their feet, leaping, drum the air, disappear into a dancing flame, liquid-weaving in fingers teasing, revealing with bedazzling grace some deeper wisdom of the heart. Beating, beating *molten* flame. Faster their mantra-dancing-mirror-whirl… Ecstasy burns in their mortal forms; faster, faster with the music; merge-merging, one self in the other, yet never touching…

Crescendo: rising to a breathless, beating, dancing, clapping, thunderous peak. The marriage of flesh and spirit. One.

Bosoms heaving, the two lovers sink to the floor. The Queen, shifting, leans against the wall, draws her lover into her arms. Bending, she presses a long kiss on her blooded lips… reverent hush.

Sidelong glances; the women are assessing my reaction.

I'm overwhelmed. My hands – all hands – explode in rapturous applause.

A warm sunny morning. The prison courtyard is quiet, the women going about their daily business. What is different is a new warmth in their eyes – toward me.

Queen Candi and her beloved have emerged – sleepily, softly, in a light breath of cloth and perfume they pass by me, a warm-shy, trusting smile upon their faces.

What a story theirs must be. Who did the Queen murder? Her beloved's husband? And is it their love for each other that's cast them from their homes, their hills, their gardens, their tribes?

## thirty-two

It is Monday, my *tenth* day in this prison. Is it Monday? The days are beginning to blur. Maybe it is my illness. The sameness of the days: time-locked.

*Diary:*
*How slowly time passes now that illness controls my flesh. Life itself seems reluctant to carry me on its daily merry-go-round and the minutes crawl. Meanwhile, internally, my spirit in stasis, millions of feverishly hurrying tiny teeth work around the clock to saw me into pieces. Blood-pink, my intestines are the first to pass away.*

I like these women – or rather the atmosphere of their beings, as I have no link to their speech; but I am a foreigner – my language, face, race, mind do not belong here.

I look at my watch. 10.15am.

*Waiting.*

10.30am.

'No think,' Sediqua says to me, as she has so often in these past days.

10.50am.

1.30pm.

'No think.' I am weary of this endless, 'No think.'

At 2pm the policewoman and the clerk cross the mud courtyard on their way home. Leaving.

I have been forgotten...

3.30pm. The jovial girl from my cell helps me to wash my clothes. Insists in a fervour of gesticulation that *she* wash my clothes. I insist, with equal fervour, that she does so at the well and *not* the drain where the women usually wash their clothes and cooking pans. Here the water sits and is unclean.

This girl is like a young and plump madonna; embracing, soft, youthfully maternal. But she shows no mercy to my clothes: beating, slapping them on the concrete, wringing them, rewashing, beating, slapping, wringing...

Finally hanging them out to dry. With laughter and familiarity. A grab of my hips, a tease, a song; a touch of kindness.

I do not return to the cell with the jovial girl. Instead, so as to avoid Sediqua's persecutory 'no think', I remain in the mud courtyard sitting on the hemp-rope bed, hunting through my memory for the next lines of that haunting poem,

> *...I sit enthroned in paradise, a sphinx not understood,*
> *A snow-cold heart uniting with the whiteness of the swan,*
> *Abhorring any action that may displace a line;*

'No think, no think,' Sediqua calls as she looks through the cell door toward me.

> *Never with tears or smiles do I disturb my attitude...*

'No think, Sediqua,' I wearily reply.

At eight o'clock I brush my teeth, wash my mouth and clean my brush with a glass of tea. Swallow it, as there is nowhere to spit but the loo or the well. The other women do not brush their teeth.

My sleep is punctuated by the women's snoring, the soldiers' roars and again that pain-filled bellow.

Another day. Not awake, not asleep.

I do what I've done every other day, sit up, tell myself to 'put-pull on your cotton slacks, pullover, *push* yourself up. Clutch your belly. Crush the pain.' Gurgles.

Over to the hellhole.

The well, and the usual morning crowd of women and children. I'm not in the mood. *Don't* smile at me, flock around me, stare at me as if I am some strange, outer-space *thing*.

Back to my cell. Hot tea, fluid in my body. A tomato, a piece of nan. 'No,' to the prison maid who is offering me a plate of hot fat and rice.

*Peel* this tomato, I tell myself. Suck it. Break the nan. Chew it. Swallow.

I want to sleep, but the mats are all rolled up and the women are sitting on the platform. There is no space to lie down, no privacy.

'There is no privacy.' No one understands what I'm saying.

Lean against the wall. I now have a wall spot, a place to lean my back during the hours of the days.

It's just morning but already it feels like – already it *is* – a long day. I need something to do, to distract myself. I doodle in my diary, like a child: Red, black and blue.

*Red – for gnosis (nature).*
*Blue – for beneficence (the higher world).*
*Black – for passion and bewilderment (the material body)...*

The red watching eye of an octopus-bird, shell shapes in blue, eye circles in black... unending.

White spaces.

Empty space.

Gravity grounded.

Leaning against the wall. Staring. Staring at the five women, watching the monotony. It fills their mouths as almost unceasing mouthfuls of food; obsessive yearning. Their bodies are pulpy with fat and lack of exercise.

Their slurping is becoming unbearable. It's the confined space... *claustrophobic...*

Outside, on the shaded veranda, I sit on my heels, Afghan-style. I feel – am – no more than three feet tall. It's comfortable.

The children are coming over. They stare, their small hands reaching toward me. A touch. *Touches.* They want me to play the game again.

Too feeble to indulge them I slip away, into my mind, into vagary.

# thirty-three

*Diary:*
*A separate reality is that of the self stolen from self,*
*voiceless,*
*snap-taut*
*Enclosed!*
*Sleep, that dark Void, free of ever-watching eyes, offers the only release.*
*But there's never enough.*

Are they days that have passed? I am desperate now, for medical attention, and for the call to come.

'Vic-toRR-iaa!'

A voice is calling from the other side of the courtyard!

Mercy, mercy, is my prayer as the soldier marches me toward the prosecutors' office…

Is that *his* balding head I see among that knot of men over on my right? The Minister of Police?

Mercy, mercy… I keep my eyes to the ground.

An asphyxiating silence. I'm begging from my heart. A contempt colder than a mountain wind closes around my bowed and naked head.

In my heart I have committed no crime. I am desperate. Looking up: 'When am I going to be released?'

'Tomorrow,' the chief prosecutor's voice. He's not looking at me. Will not look at me. In their minds I am corrupt. A Western whore whose very presence defiles.

Tomorrow comes. And goes.

Is it Friday?

'Vic-toRR-iaa.'

Hurry – hurrying as fast as my sick body will go, to the visitors' grate, my heart racing with hope.

A young soldier, saying his only English: 'Tomorrow, maybe tomorrow.'

Visitors' day again. It must be Saturday.

I stay in the cell with Marjohn and the eldest mother. Fragile, too fragile to move.

The old woman is not in her corner. She is sitting close to the cell window, looking out toward the visitors' area. So quiet. *So* quiet that I often forget she's in here. She is different from the others – slim, and her costume is another style: a long black neck-high dress rather than the brilliantly coloured pantaloons and dress-smocks worn by the others. A rusty key hangs from a piece of string around her neck. A seeker of solace through a meditative introspection, she looks as if she belongs to the deserts or mountains. Somewhere hidden yet expansive.

She looks different today. Or is it that she feels different, to me? Sorrow, her sorrow – how acutely I feel it. How many years, how many forgotten, unvisited, imprisoned years has she silently passed here, sitting cobwebbed in her white gossamer of veil? And yet how wisdomly-lovely she is.

Marjohn, dressed in her flowing mauve top and frilled lace pantaloons, unwraps boxes of biscuits brought by her mother, who sits cross-legged on the platform watching her. Marjohn removes the biscuits from their containers, arranges them on the platform: yellow cakes, blue biscuits. A red, green and white iced cake forms a double circle in the middle. Double-layered black biscuits, shortbread sprinkled with hundreds and thousands…

Marjohn sits back, leans her head on her mother's shoulder. A sad silent rapport. The garish biscuits are their focus, distraction from their sorrow.

They are shared and greedily devoured by the others as they filter back into the cell.

Night. Queen Candi knows to choose a moment when Sediqua and the two maids are out. She's been watching me of late. It's a fixed, almost predatory stare. No speech.

Her face is close to mine, her green-brown eyes commanding me to accompany her out into the night.

I follow her shadow – toward the hellhole?

She, we, disappear into the pitch black at the base of the steps. I can't see her, but I can feel her animal energy. The Queen is nervous, excited. There is something in her hand. A squeak of metal, a lid being unscrewed.

A tiny glint of light – a glass bottle is being passed in the darkness. She wants me to drink. But what is it? Queen Candi is breathing on me, impelling me to obey her. She is the Queen, the ruler of this Kabul prison.

*Grunt* – not to be disobeyed…

I drink.

It's not hashish. It's not mufarah. It's a thick, gritty, syrupy *foul*-tasting liquid. Some sort of medicine?

A soft *growl-purr*. The Queen is pleased. Is now striding ahead of me – lest she be seen? She has vanished. The throat-gripping goo guu-ulps its way thickly down my throat.

Back in the cell I lean into a corner. A subtle change in the atmosphere. The women are still talking, but their backs are turned to me. Is it to do with my going out with the Queen?

Heaviness. Suspended time.

Why won't Sediqua, someone, turn and look at me, rescue me from this resounding silence, this imploding non-existence?

Heaviness.

I'm invisible. They can't see me.

It's the *corner*; its walls are *sucking* me in, dissolving me, trading their inert dreariness for my *life*.

I try to scream for help but my throat, it's blocked, is entombed by a Golgothan boulder. No sound can escape.

The women's backs are immobile; a row of low soft hills turned to stone. Transmogrified. No longer flesh and blood.

I *have* to move.

*Crawl-ing* to the platform's edge. *Sliiiiding* down.

*Crawl-ing* across this stone floor, round smoothness.

Crawling, dragging myself onto the verandah. Where are my legs?

I drag my body to the veranda's edge… edge of consciousness… see her: a crone, with mouth agape and empty stare. Death face staring…

*Splash!*

Liquid melting.

*Splash!* She is changing into a wizened old woman, warmly gazing down at me through the fuzzy night light. She's open-mouthed, hag-toothed, smiling. An empty bucket in her hand. She's brought me back.

Rivulets of water down my face. Blink. Water of life.

Thank you.

She sinks back into night.

Wet. Now shiveringly wet. My throat hurts – my mouth, is it bleeding? *Freezing.* Uncontrollable shaking. Tears. The stench of vomit.

Unseen, the lioness prowls back – carnivorous, lungeing-lusting, green-brown eyes, black-stone pupils *spinning* into mine – bewitching her prey?

Total, sober, fascinated surprise. How can eyes spin like that?

Queen Candi's face is suddenly flushing with shame. She lowers her head… drops to her knees.

I can feel her hands lifting my foot. Now the other. Rolling up my sodden jeans. Peeling off my socks. Drying my feet with her apron. *Warming* them. Giving me succour.

Strong arms – hers – are around me, assisting me to a hemp-rope bed. Telling someone something.

Another bed has appeared – for her? Is she going to sleep next to me?

A woman's scolding voice. Marie. She is *furious* with Queen Candi.

Quiet.

Silence seeps.

*Spinning.*

Night heavy.

*Spinning.*

*Spinning.*

In black unconscious… seeing – a circle. Lovers… head to head, toe to toe… *spinning* …a vision of…

…the *sphinx*, gazing enigmatically upward, into…

> *…my mirrors pure, which make all things on earth more beautiful,*
> *my eyes, my great and wondrous eyes with light perpetual.*

Eternity? O…

Falling…

Floating…
*infinitely* infinitesimal…within the Cosmos.
The pupil of the sphinx's eye.

Sediqua is shaking me awake to a sharp bright sun.

'Victoria, you good, very *good* person, you, Victoria.'

A wide, true smile is on her face. Is this what the tension of last night was about – a fear that I would succumb to their Queen? They must have known she had fed me that drug, known her intention. Have they been waiting for this moment since the first day? Waiting, watching, not missing a trick.

Catharsis. Order reigns. In me their prison peace is secure. I am an outsider. And now they know it.

'Queen Candi?'

'Sick. She in bed.'

I can hear Marie. She's singing.

The gooey syrup I swallowed was an opiate, of that I have no doubt. An almost deadly one? My body feels light, separate from me.

The sky is blue, the same pale blue as on the first day of my imprisonment. Unchanged, unchanging. A vast glass wall; sky prison.

Where are you cloud; little cloud, old cloud, large cloud, whatever-shaped, changing cloud?

A bird? Where are you swallow? Crow? Sparrow? Pigeon?

*Please* break this porcelain blue.

Nothing.

Return to earth. Solid, textured, coloured, *irregular*. How ancient those bricks and cracked walls look, their edges softened from decades of slow disintegration: aeons of containment.

This bed is my containment. My support.

Faces. Women and children are bending over me, black eyes staring greedily at my blue. They threaten what little sense of self I have left. Strange loud-energied animals: I close them out, shut my eyes.

They are moving away.

Now it's flies. Small flies fast-walk over my hands, stopping, proboscises stamping-sucking. Stealing minuscule droplets of my life's fluid. Whirl-buzz; two, copulating, crash-land on my arm.

Zooooom. A wasp?

The almond blossoms are dying, minute by minute, as the day passes. Singly, in pairs, threes. Melting from the leafy branches into a ragged pink circle upon the grey-brown earth.

A trinity of urchins with knotted hair have spied the fallen blossoms. The two girls dart toward them, quickly pick out the most perfect. Sitting, thread them into bracelets for their wrists. The boy is crushing them underfoot.

I am without pain.

## thirty-four

*Diary:*
*How long is it before a prisoner becomes a prisoner? A day, a week, a month, a year? 'A day that is a year, a year whose day is long.'*

The days drift by, each coming to layer me with further fading hope.

'Vic-toRR-iaa!'

The ritual is the same. The men in their office. 'Where did you visit in Afghanistan?'

'Ka…'

'Where did you visit…'

It is all a perverse, sadistic game of power.

'I'm a tourist. Tourist!' They don't hear me, don't see me. In their narrow, eye-averted minds I do not exist. They are never going to release me.

With each step back toward the prison door I feel… *lighter.*

I no longer care.

With the closing of the door all my desire to know and belong to the world has gone.

Has lifted like a weight from my being.

*Peace.* I feel so at peace. The battle of wills is over. I have relinquished my will, and in doing so have been strangely freed. The person I was is gone, has centred itself in detachment. In 'no think'. This prison, my refuge.

Do they sense this?

On Thursday my name is called.

On Saturday my name is called.

Sunday. I cross to the visitors' grate. Again, a soldier, saying: 'Tomorrow, tomorrow.'

'Victooriiaaa.'

It must be Tuesday.

'Victooriiaaa.' I'm now almost afraid to hear my name.

I sit on the chair, do not look at my tormentors.

Two words: 'Cameras confiscated.'

My precious, magic connection-reflection with the universal self is being stolen. I am too weak to hide my grief.

The women. They see the edge beckoning. Are reaching to help.

They lead me to a hidden room. Gently strip me of my clothes. Sit me on a stool. Wash me...

Water.

*Waterfalls.*

Soap bubble hands, lightly skimming… washing away those stains within, without.

Collapsing on a bed in the midday sun, I feel my spirit… *fading.* I am dying.

*Mother Earth, set me free.*

Am I outside, gazing up at the night stars? Or am I inside, gazing at the stars in my mind?

A vibration, a shaking; a shrill, multi-toned shrilling… The women, they're pulling me back into consciousness.

'Go, go – Go! Vic-tor-ia!' They're so excited, shouting: '*You Go!*' They are lifting me up. One holds my suitcase.

'Go, go!' they cry, helping me to the prison gate.

'Tashakur, tashakur, tashakur.' It is the one word I know to say, breathe:

Thank you.

# part three

*And everywhere the ceremony of innocence is drowned.*
W.B. Yeats

## thirty-five

'It's been touch and go.'

We are walking through the centre of the judicial zone; the consul is speaking to me.

'The majority of the prosecutors were against granting you bail. If it hadn't been for the Governor of Kabul we couldn't have got bail. By the way, he has ordered that your camera equipment be returned to you.'

Something flutters in my chest. Subtle, butterfly-like.

'As a condition of your bail you are to stay at the Behzad Hotel.' He is looking me over as he walks and talks. Appraising me? 'By the look of you it would pay to have yourself medically checked.' He stops, scribbles something on a notepad. The name of a hospital, and the address of the Behzad Hotel.

We have passed the prosecutors' block and are walking through a block of buildings that I vaguely recall as if from another life. This was where I was taken after I was arrested at the airport. I have now passed beyond the familiar… am now stepping toward the main gate.

*Exhilaration.* Magnificent *expanse* – the small space before my next step is so…

*…huge!*

*Wonderful wonderful space… the hills in the distance… the release…*

Why is he sucking in his breath, pompously muttering?

'…the Dane's bail.'

The smuggler and I share the same file. He has to be released before I can begin court proceedings. The consul is confident that his release can be secured within the week.

The consul opens the taxi door for me, tells the driver where I'm to go.

I thank him. 'That was a *very* long night.'

'You're very lucky to have been released so soon. In fact, you've made history by this early release. It is quite normal to be held for upwards of three months before bail is granted.'

A comfortable worn leather seat. And an open window. Wind, a warm rush of wind massages my face, hum-echoing in my ear.

The streets are filled with a moving blur – dreamlike images. Nothing is static. Streams of vehicles, buildings, mules, beggars, hawkers, a camel, pedestrians. Everything and everyone *everywhere*. A buzzing, humming, beeping *delicious maelstrom…*

The taxi stops halfway along a small street at the gates of a run-down single-storey hotel. The Behzad. Mustn't forget my suitcase.

I'm within twenty feet of the hotel porch when I notice him: a grey-blue figure with a grey Afghan cap on his head, perching on a concrete ledge, his knees folded into his chest, elbows jutting out like half-folded wings, hands hanging limply over his knees. More gargoyle than human. Apart from the intensity of his gaze and the blue smoke coiling from the cigarette between his fingers, he's immobile. Is observing me.

What sounds like the word 'room' issues from his throat as I draw near. His eyes are bloodshot, hooded. I nod my head. He unfolds, revealing himself to be thin and quite tall. I follow in his wake of stale tobacco smoke to a makeshift reception desk. He sidles in behind it and pulls out a tattered book. Yellow-brown nicotine-stained fingers open the register. I sign my name.

Without speaking, the gargoyle uplifts my suitcase, leads me along a dingy but homely passageway, hands me a key and leaves.

The walls are stucco white, pleasingly irregular. A light bulb hangs from the ceiling. A hemp-rope bed, with mattress and pillow. I lock the door, sit on the bed.

*My* room! A small wooden bedside cabinet, and an artisan's table in the centre of the room. A squat yellow candle in a battered tin holder, a dirty cracked clay ashtray. One comfortable-looking string-bottomed armchair, and a less comfortable-looking chair (similar to the ones in the prosecutors' office) in a corner near a pair of thin white curtains. What's behind them?

*Delight:* A set of narrow glass-panelled French doors opening out to a dusty concrete yard bordered by a high wooden fence. A door opening in and a door opening out: the power to open what is shut, to shut what is open. My own set of keys! Perfect!

First I need to have a shower.

The bathroom is along the hallway, smelly but clean. The weak spray of water is river cold. Refreshing.

I peer into a small eroded mirror above the basin. *Shock!* Who are you, staring – bewildered and greenish, face thin, familiar-eyed? Are you me?

Back in my room I rummage through my suitcase looking for my Indian cotton dress. It feels so light: transforming, refined, fragile.

Assilan crosses my thoughts. If he is thinking of me he must think I'm far away.

I open my French doors. A shaft of sunlight slips across the floor. I lie on my bed. A warm grassy smell wafts in, accompanied by the comforting sound of something munching – hay?

*Heaven.*

## thirty-six

Another battered taxi takes me to the hospital recommended by the consul.

I have, according to a doctor's microscope, a particularly nasty variety of amoebic dysentery. Over the next two weeks I have to swallow a bucketful of large white tablets. Bitter pills for my initiation back into the city of Kabul.

Waking anew to my freedom.

Walking outside the hotel's gates.

Wandering cautiously around the nearby streets.

The city has changed: it's more crowded and 'foreign' than I remember and the approaching summer has coated it with a dusty, thirsty face. In prison I'd yearned to be returned to the world but now that I'm back in it, I feel *small* and so very inconsequential.

Can they – do they – read this in my unarmoured being?

'Baksheesh, baksheesh – free, free.' Fur merchants hang around outside their shops. 'Baksheesh… free.' Fingers, a finger beckons. He points to the curtains of fur jackets, coats. Then indoors to his back room. 'Five minutes,' a leering sickly grin. 'Baksheesh, baksheesh.' It is the same all down the street. They want me to have sex with them in exchange for furs.

An hour, perhaps two, spent like this and I'm relieved to be… back inside the hotel gate.

A group of assorted Europeans are at the front desk signing the hotel register, blocking access to the passageway. They're boisterous and confident and obviously intent on a good holiday. Their presence, their *unawareness*, makes me shrink… Shrinking my way between them, ignored.

It makes me want to close my door… a prisoner, closing her door. Worse, a co-prisoner whose freedom depends on the release of a stranger, the Dane.

Not even this room, nor the comfort of my mattress, offers escape from the precariousness of my reality. The uncertainty amoebically eating into me.

The hotel has a pleasantly large Persian-carpeted restaurant and lounge. And serves food.

Food: I eat frequent and measured quantities to help my body readjust to the varied diet and adapt to the medication. Taste starved, I salivate at the very smell: roasting chicken, oranges, apples, yogurt. I'm so hungry and appreciative that I splinter and suck the bones of chicken wings, dribble with gastronomic ecstasy at the sight of fried eggs, tomatoes, onions. But it is hot rice that gives the greatest comfort.

It gives sleep.

It's now three days since my release and still there's no word from the consul. I'm anxious. I need to know if the Danish and British authorities have made any progress in their bid to release the Dane. I also need to know about the return of my Hasselblad and Leica – that the Governer of Kabul has ordered their return. Almost as much as my 'freedom' I value these and, despite the prosecutors having told me that they had confiscated them, I'm not prepared to lose them, nor any of my films.

I telephone the British embassy and a very English receptionist puts me through.

The consul's voice is formal: 'Yes, Victoria, I do have the letter from the Governor, authorising the return of your equipment, it is here waiting for you to uplift it. As to the situation of your Danish counterpart, I've had numerous discussions with the Danish ambassador and we are confident he'll be released on bail in a few days. By the way, do you realise it will be in both your hands to organise your own trial?'

He is officially signing off? His job done?

I do not have a clue as to how this country's legal system operates. How could I?

He is released sooner than the consul had anticipated – two days after my call.

He's given the room adjoining mine and is just arriving.

'Come in.' His thick accent. 'Jens.'

'Victoria.'

Our rooms are much the same, except that he has two string-bottomed chairs to my one. Jens closes his door and rubs his hands in glee, eager to celebrate his release. A teacup-sized piece of hashish, plonk in the middle of the small table between us, awaits. Beyond introducing ourselves we haven't yet spoken.

I watch him as, with an air of nonchalance, he holds a lighted yellow candle to a corner of the block of dope, softening it; breaks off a piece, an inch-thick lump. He crumbles the hashish, licks and joins four outsized cigarette papers, mixes in a quantity of cigarette tobacco to build a joint that looks like a rolling pin.

He lights up and takes a long drag. A large cloud pours from his coughing lungs. Still coughing, he extends his spidery arm, inviting me to take the glowing rolling pin from between his pincer fingers. To join the 'two prisoners on bail' party.

Red embers and ash fall. My throat gasps. Choking, I reject the offer of another puff.

An extravagance of blue-white smoke floats.

Haze.

Our conversation is slow, Jens coughing himself into oblivion while wheezing to me that there are twelve Westerners on the men's side of the prison.

'Americans, British, French, heroin and opium users, some caught for stealing, some for smuggling.'

'All of them, three to six months after their arrest, are still waiting for bail.' The consul was right. I was lucky to be released so soon.

'The ones who have been convicted are doing up to ten years.'

Jens' red eyes stare blotto-ishly across at me. I don't want to know what he is telling me. I don't want to let it in. But there's more.

'There's this madman – the Neanderthal, the Yanks call him. (Cough, wheeze.) He's chained by his feet to a tree. He is very ugly. He has no brain. All he does is bellow, weep and laugh.'

'I heard him bellowing. He sounded like an animal in pain.'

'Yes, that was after the soldiers had whipped him. He is immensely strong. I wanted to beat him too, when he kept me from sleeping.'

Alarm bells ringing in me: this lean, stone-faced Scandinavian is by his own admission without compassion.

He changes the subject. 'What were you photographing in Afghanistan to have caused the CIA to come to the airport?'

He is quizzing me. Crumbles yet another hillock of hashish for yet another joint.

The broken-hearted Neanderthal vanishes from my thoughts. 'CIA?'

Silence. I'm physically shocked. Of course – the grotesque twins. But why? I didn't sneak around the country snapping the forbidden, whatever that is.

'I didn't photograph anything of interest to the CIA or any other secret police. I've been…'

Hesitation. My chest tightens. Is Jens colluding with the Afghan Police Minister, the one responsible, I'm sure, for my arrest?

Calm down. Don't be ridiculous, I tell myself. This man Jens is no more than a polished escapist fleeing into absorption and abandonment through the senses, not interested in any reality other than his own. A self-styled connoisseur of hashish caught for smuggling 'the very best'.

'I thought they were interested in drugs, in smuggling.' Jens stares across at me vacuously. 'The CIA men.'

'…uhh?' He's already somewhere else.

He's intimidatingly tall. He's male. And my freedom is fatefully twinned with his. The small mercy: I'm not alone with this nightmare.

## thirty-seven

The first step toward organising our trial is to begin, we finally discover after an arduously slow process of inquiry, in the bottom floor of the building adjoining the prosecutors' office and the prison compound. In the clerks' office. With this knowledge in hand Jens and I set out to reclaim our freedom.

We walk through Kabul's streets, busy and summery. Is it the aliveness of the day, or because we have each other for company? We are blithely optimistic.

The prison gate. The clerks' office.

Our cheerfulness soon dissipates when we discover ourselves among a wall-to-wall thick crowd of tubercular-spitting gassy-bowelled low-life criminals all awaiting pre-trial processing. We must wait our turn.

Five hours later we are still squashed amid this miasma, having received not so much as a hint that the handful of clerks are aware of us, although we presented ourselves at the counter and gave our names when we first arrived. It is now 2pm; closing time.

The next morning we tread the same path, footfall upon footfall upon footfall to the prison compound and pre-trial processing room.

And the following morning…

On day four, hot flushes of angry eloquence emerge from the hashish-eyed Jens. To no effect: the clerks appear not to hear him, nor see us.

> *Diary:*
> *Jens and I are marionettes. Prosecutors and clerks, negative masks, sending us stiff faced into the concrete labyrinth of Kabul. A deadly theatre?*
> *Dead ends?*

Seven such days have passed.

Day eight, and it eventually dawns that the clerks are expecting a bribe. We can read it in their eyes.

We decide to stand our ground. Jens will intimidate them with his height, an impressive six foot six (or more), and I will pierce their resistance with my scalpel eyes.

A further seven days pass, and we have made no progress. Once again, time is an instrument of torture.

The summer heat is beginning. By 8.30am the temperature is already in the mid-seventies Fahrenheit. And rising with the heat are the city's smells, especially that of rotting sewage. Kabul's sewer system is a network of open drains unchanged, to all appearances, since the days of the first empires.

Wide channels narrow to stone bottoms, and one of these drains runs alongside the footpath we use every day to reach the prison. Its intensifying stench is becoming intolerable and however diligent I am about trying to avoid it, my peripheral vision never fails to catch a black *bubbling* turgid mess of human waste. It's so foul that even the flies have abandoned it.

The single benefit of the awfulness of this daily trek is that it serves to strengthen our resolve.

## thirty-eight

Eighteen days from the day we first set out, the clerks finally give way. The file is removed from their control and passes into the hands of two prosecutors appointed by the Court of Narcotics. We have an appointment with them at 10am the day after tomorrow.

9.57am. We're at the doorway into the prosecutors' office, nervously priming ourselves for our meeting. Although the gulf between our mindsets has made Jens and I reluctant conversants – to me he is no more than a tall pale shadow – we now know each other reasonably well. And know that this is the meeting that will decide our fates.

10am. Did we knock, or did this smiling, welcoming, black-suited little man open it for us? And shake our hands? We enter the coffin-shaped office of the two prosecutors.

The recognition is immediate: the prosecutors are without individuality. They have so identified with their roles as to be caricatures, not people. There is something terrifying about this 'real-unrealness'. It is the same feeling I had when I was paraded before and interrogated by the prosecutors during my imprisonment. There's no conscience.

Physically the two prosecutors are alike: thin, beakish, small. But in their emotional expression they are each the antithesis of the other. The door opener, the sickly-sweet smiler who welcomed us in, is the 'disarmer', the overly-familiar long-lost friend. His partner, sunk behind his huge desk, exudes a cold omnipotence, his small black eyes already in the act of locking us up. His nose is large and as sharp as his bony face and thin line of lip. Quite a photograph. He is the decider.

The sickly-sweet smiler, smiling, touches my elbow and leads me over to one of two chairs close to his partner's desk.

I am sincerely demure as I sit before him.

'I will ask for you to be imprisoned,' he says to me, his voice frozen behind his frozen lips. The meeting is over.

Not one word to Jens. Or was he there? I haven't registered.

The 'disarmer', closing the door behind us, has followed us outside. He wants to speak to me. Jens is already walking off, is leaving me stranded with this diminutive man.

What does he want? Why is he so whisperingly flea-hoppingly hanging about me?

'I can help you. I will talk to my friend, you beautiful girl. I personally organise you have "not-guilty" verdict; my rest-pond-sibility. You stay Behzad Hotel, yes?'

He knows where I am staying?

'Today, this afternoon, I visit to talk my arrangements for you.'

Can this weasely little sniveller actually help me? I so want to believe that he can.

## thirty-nine

In the course of Jens' and my to-ing and fro-ing between the Behzad Hotel and the prison compound we had finally found a route through the city that was free of open sewers. But as it took longer than the usual path we only used it on our return.

I return to my hotel via this route, stopping in a tourist cafe to eat a bowl of yogurt and fruit salad, my usual mid-morning fare.

The remainder of the walk takes in a street of antique shops, and another of gemstone shops. I peer through the glass – into universes of polished blue: cloudy, gold-speckled oceans of hard stone, sky-soft, lapis lazuli. And a glimmer of hope.

Then back; through the streets of fox furs and 'baksheesh'; past the gargoyle leering from his perch, back to my room with my French doors ajar, listening to the familiar munching of the grey-white mare tethered in the far corner of the dusty and narrow concrete yard outside.

Almost three weeks since I first set foot inside here I also know the hotel set-up. I've discovered that the gargoyle, who is the hotel manager not the owner, is a prodigious smoker of hashish and keeps Jens supplied. His red-bleary gutterish eyes have attempted to entice me to be another of his customers, but have failed. My survival depends upon my having a clear head.

The hotel also has a cheerful and kindly live-in cook who has a wife and young daughter; and a servant, a beaten-faced surly youth whose duty is 'room service' and sweeping up. The gargoyle keeps a red-eyed watch, moving from his perch only when it's time to feed the muncher of hay, the tethered mare, or when a new guest arrives.

For the remainder, the hotel is abuzz with the loud feet and voices of the European tourists, the majority of whom are a party of Danes. Company for Jens.

For the most I have no choice but to keep my own company, much of which is spent sleeping. And my body needs to sleep: it's battling chemical warfare and an invasion of the lowliest of life forms.

I usually sleep in the afternoon, after Jens and I return from our stand-offs with the clerks.

It is now 3.30pm, and although I'm pretending to myself that I'm not agitated I know I am. My tired body, tired mind are sinking toward afternoon repose, succumbing to sleep…

Purposeful footsteps are stomping through my head. Outside my room?

A knock at the door.

The freshly oiled and combed 'disarmer' stands there with the servant boy and a cowering stranger who introduces himself as the hotel owner.

They are crowding into my sanctuary, which rapidly fills with the reek of a cheap cologne – the prosecutor's. And someone's stale sweat.

'Madam be moved, *now*. This room not suitable for madam.'

The prosecutor feigns disgust; orders the owner to order the servant to pick up my suitcase. Or so I surmise from his plumped-up manner and the others' subservience.

The prosecutor is all toothy smiles to me – seems to think he is doing me a favour by making me leave my room and accompany his odiferous person. The meek hotelier and the obedient servant both avoid my questioning eye.

A lock turns, a door opens and I am shown into a generously proportioned and exotically decorated room with Persian carpets. And a large double bed with rich red covers. The bed shouts out *Sex*.

Satisfied that the room is 'suitable for madam', the prosecutor demands a bottle of red wine.

He locks the door. Sits down and pours me a glass. Smiles his weaselish smile. I'm polite, pretending that I'm not aware of the obvious.

He gulps, one, two glassfuls.

Politely distant small-talking.

Three glassfuls.

My strategy isn't working; his facade of gentlemanly concern is giving way. He fixes me with a silly schoolboy grin, stands up and points to the bed. 'You, me.' Is coming toward me.

He is puny and underdeveloped, no match for me in terms of physical strength. I know that with one judo shift of the hip I could fling him across the room. I also know that to do so would be to sign my own death warrant.

I suppress the urge to fight him; instead leap up from my chair and back away... shrinking as far away from the bed as possible.

I am against the wall. The prosecutor is approaching, undisguised glee in his eyes and a twisted grin across his mouth...

I want to *shrink through* this wall behind me. He's pressing his weedy body against mine...

Suddenly it's as if a floodgate in me has been opened by this pathetic little man. A tidal wave of despair surges through me and takes possession – of the prosecutor too; his face too is crumpling – he is beginning to weep. Is weeping on my shoulder. Blowing his nose on a white handkerchief.

Now he is hugging me paternally, protectively, apologising. Stepping back.

I pick up my suitcase and return to my humble room. Desolate, angry. Knowing that as a prisoner inside jail I'd been *safe;* now as a prisoner on the outside I'm *accessible* to those who hold my file – *the keepers of the law.*

It is Jens who suggests a solution.

'You have to buy your freedom, Victoria. I have someone who is going to help me – my business partner and the son of a government minister.'

This explains his laid-back air of confidence.

'My friend has suggested that $1000 US will buy my innocence. You need a friend too – someone who has direct access to the chief judge at the Court of Narcotics. The clerks and prosecutors have no power. You will need money.'

Jens obviously knows the system here. Or his friend does.

Two possible 'helpers' flash through my mind. The first is the Buddha-eyed, aristocratic Assilan, who believes that his traveller-photographer friend is by now back in her homeland.

Although he has appeared in my thoughts I have thus far refrained from contacting him. A perverse pride has held me back, and given me to believe that I could extricate myself from this situation on my own. But I can't.

Hesitantly I dial Assilan's number.

The Persian voice answers. 'Hello Assilan…'

I can hear it in his voice – he's shocked to learn that I am still in Afghanistan. But he's my only chance, my only hope: I have to tell him.

'I have been charged with smuggling hashish and am about to be sentenced to imprisonment.'

Silence.

Finally he speaks. He is changing the subject; is telling me about his impending medical examinations. He sounds nervous. Is it because we are talking on a telephone? Or that he doesn't want to know me?

*Warm heat.* My tension melts. We are to meet, within the hour, upstairs at an American-style coffee house.


## forty

He is sitting opposite me, listening as I tell him my story – the 'one night', into the forgotten days, release, into the 'now'; the *gladness* I feel in his being here with me.

He's *very* quiet. Thinking.

Lifting his eyes, to mine. 'Your person has aroused the anger of the conservative element here. These men are jealous and prejudiced and see you in a distorted way. It makes no difference if you have committed a crime or if you are innocent.'

What is he saying?

'These men, these type of people are not educated. And they will want to punish you. They are a danger to anyone who is a freethinker. Myself included.'

A pause. A deep sense of apprehension.

'Don't worry, I promise you I will see that you are freed.'

Do I hear him, his soothing voice, saying…

He's going to save me. *Oh, a friend, saviour friend, Assilan!*

But he has enemies, he says, who, if they were to discover that he is assisting me, would have him arrested and imprisoned. It would be the end of his medical career. I understand the gravity of his words.

To avoid endangering him we are not to walk on the streets together. I must at all times walk at a short distance behind him. Should we ever be questioned, I am to say that he works as a translator for the British embassy.

Assilan agrees that a bribe is the only way to persuade the judge of the Court of Narcotics to return my freedom. He also agrees that $1000 US, which I would give to him to give to the judge, would be sufficient (the judge's annual salary is $2000).

To back up the Governor's letter and get my cameras and film back I will probably need another $1000. It may be a relatively small amount, but I have no money.

Assilan glances at his watch, I at the exquisite moon-arcs over his lowered eyelids. Cradle in their beauty.

He has to go; he has a class at the university in half an hour. He switches into an impersonal mode. This is a serious business. My task is to obtain the funds and phone him as soon as the money has been transferred. In the interim he will speak to the chief judge on my behalf.

*Diary:*
*Money. Money or Freedom. Money and Freedom. Freedom from money. I need freedom, and money. Money for freedom. Love gives freedom, and sometimes money to buy freedom.*
    *Who?*

The image of my Aunt Marion, my *rich* Aunt Marion who lives in elitist detachment on the top floor of an exclusive apartment block in upper class Toronto, flashes across my mind. She is cold, ice-perfect, fragile, sits enthroned on one of her long grey-blue brushed silk settees in an overly large pale cream-green lounge as people the size of ants walk the streets below. I visited her briefly when I was nineteen.

I flash back to myself as then – cruising in sleek superiority behind the darkened glass of a long black chauffeur-driven limousine. Stopping at traffic lights. Peering through the darkened glass at pedestrians staring back with reverent curiosity… The traffic lights turn green.

My aunt is my mother's twin sister. Acidic with wealth, she is ultra-conservative, and an avid collector of miniatures. She could help me. But will she?

'No international.' The gargoyle's nicotine-stained fingers are upon the hotel's one telephone. He's not going to let me use it. 'Post office.'

Waving down a taxi. 'Post office.'

'Telephone?'

'Outside,' a teller tells me, waving his hand in the direction of the world. I dart through the traffic toward a red, doorless standard phone booth positioned in the centre of a traffic island in what has to be Kabul's busiest and noisiest intersection.

Nervously dialling my aunt's number. There is static, crackling. A remote sounding, *ring-ring, ring-ring…*

'Hallow.' My aunt!

'Aunt Marion,' I'm shouting.

'Hallow.' She sounds tired, distant, and with the static crackling and traffic noise almost inaudible. Now, nothing. The line's gone dead.

But she is *there*, my brittle-ishly snobbish, su-pearl-atively dressed, ivory-towered, razor-witted, witheringly judgemental and sporadically generous and loving aunt is *there*.

I dial her number again.

'Hallow?'

'Aunt Marion!'

'Vicki, iz-that-yoou?' Her voice sounds like it's reverberating from the end of the earth.

'Yes, yes, Aunt Marion. I'm in *Afghanistan*. I've had an *Accident*. I need *$2000* dollars urgently.'

'Are you all orrright?'

She's in a human mood, thank goodness.

I'm having to shout. 'Yes, but please send $2000 …British embassy, Kabul, Afghanistan, otherwise …*Prison*.'

The static is terrible. 'Prizin?'

Silence. The telephone is dead and my heart thumping.

Three days later a phone call. The British consul says they have received $3000 in my name. Aunt Marion has saved me!

There's more good news when I meet with Assilan at the American coffee house. The chief judge of the Court of Narcotics has agreed to find me not guilty on condition of the payment of $1000. The trial will be set as soon as the money is paid. Jens must have already organised his release.

I have the cash, all $3000 of it, hidden in my hotel room. The consul had handed it over to me when I visited him yesterday. He had asked no questions. Assilan will come with me now and collect a thousand of it.

In accordance with our code I remain at a distance behind Assilan as we walk to the Behzad. He waits outside while I go in and get the cash. I follow him into a small empty alleyway.

He slips the ten hundred-dollar bills into his inside jacket pocket. The deal is done.

## forty-one

*Diary:*
*New phase. Concrete forms move as changing personalities flit across the stage.*
*Nerves leap, insomnia speaks in the dark and empty night. Demons enter cloaked in poisonous thoughts, and the flesh exudes hell's faeces with its filthy smells.*
*Mother Earth, I beseech you: Free me from the vain laws of Men. And the stabbing pains of sickness which steal my natural happiness and leave me open to despair.*
*Let me Soon, over your prison of mountains, home, to love and peace.*

Long and sharply black shadows are moving across the chalk-white earth. They are directly ahead of us, and are at least twelve feet long; Jens' longer – a power pylon.

The trial has been set for 9am and we are a nervous fifteen minutes early. Adding to my nervousness is an unaccountable feeling of depression, which could be medically based, as despite my obediently swallowing 164 stomach-gripping anti-amoeba pills these rampantly self-divisible low-lifes remain within me.

It's five minutes to nine. Assilan has come! And Jens' business partner. They are standing a few feet apart, about twenty feet from where we are. Assilan signals to me with his eyes, telling me he will wait where he is.

It's time to go in.

My photographic eye immediately awakens. Archangel light floods into the room through a large square window behind the judge. He, ork-hunched over his desk on his raised platform, is a pure black silhouette. Wearing black-lensed sunglasses.

An inner shudder, he is the *archetypal satanic*. A black-white room.

We're to sit below him. Below his radiant-haloed, black being.

The sunlight floods into my eyes, almost blinding me. The light is bouncing off his sunglasses and the reams of paper he's flicking through.

His sunglasses pivot toward us. He's looking down at us. Is saying something to a clerk, who asks us to leave the room, to go outside and wait. Obediently we do, and sit on the hard bench near the courtroom door.

After ten minutes the clerk re-emerges. He passes us, comes back carrying a tray, a teapot and a glass. Jens and I are too nervous to utter so much as a squeak.

Another ten minutes. We shuffle our bodies. The bench is hard.

The clerk is summoning us back.

Jens is the first to be 'tried'. He stands. The silhouette is signing papers, handing them to a reverential clerk, who pronounces the verdict: 'Not guilty.'

Jens is thanking the judge, is featherlike with relief. I can feel it emanating from him as he sits down.

My turn. Standing. *Tense-tension.* He's taking a little more time. I can't see his eyes. Only black glass.

The papers are again signed, and again passed to the clerk, who hands them to another. The verdict: 'One year's imprisonment.'

Dark *dread* engulfs my gut.

'Do you agree with this verdict?' The silhouette, addressing me from his sepulchral throne.

'No,' I choke, tiny-voiced.

'You have the right of appeal.'

The trial is over.

Jellyishly wobbling back down the stairs and out, toward Assilan; telling him the verdict. His eyes flash, narrow with anger, toward the courtroom. He gestures to me – hand extended, palm spread, a small downward movement – to wait where I am, and dashes over to the courtroom.

He reappears, trying to control his anger. Voice rapid: 'I asked the judge why he did not release you and he threatened to charge me with attempted blackmail. The money is lost but I will talk to my father. He is a general and friend of the Deputy Minister of Justice. With their help we will have you released. Don't worry.'

Assilan's calming 'Don't worry.'

A taxi back to the Behzad. I open my French doors, sink onto my bed. I don't have the strength to worry.

I can hear a familiar loud coughing – a jubilant Jens, a self-professed *professional* smuggler, is in his room smoking himself stupid. Celebrating. He also must have opened his French doors as the prevailing wisp of breeze carries aromatic clouds curling out of his room, through my open doors.

Following them with my eyes… wafting vaporously toward me.

Seductively de-scen-ding.

Black sleep.

A male voice, ringing out. High, pure, hauntingly beautiful: a heart caress of *beautiful sound*. A thousand fingers are knocking, tapping, rolling upon a tabla.

My head lolls; pillow-soft. Eyes still closed, half asleep, listening.

A piano accordion is sucking, billowing, sharp effusive melodies. Harmonising with its consort, a Middle Eastern ancestor of the violin. Flowing through the wall alongside my bed… impelling me to rise, to find its source. Within the hotel's Persian rug-bedecked lounge.

Bowing to us, his arms outstretched, he releases his feet to a drumming, spinning, extraordinary dance. They are a troupe of nomads supplementing their livelihood by performing for the season's garrulous tourists.

Their wild, fantastic music fills the night, my soul.

# forty-two

*Diary:*

*The judgement room: the voices of men are all that is heard. Their laws, hungry jaws, snap – snapped – upon a free soul.*

*Reality hits: wraith-like, illusionless. My money has been stolen. I have been sentenced to a year's imprisonment by a thief and a liar – the chief judge of the Court of Narcotics. And Jens is free. The smuggler is freed.*

*How can I have faith? I now have such little faith…*

A conservatively cheerful Jens pokes his head through the open doors.

'Would you like to come for a ride with me and my friend Faruk? We are going to have a picnic in the countryside.'

I haven't been out of the city for what feels like months.

The three of us squash in the front of the Land Rover. Faruk, Jens' streetwise 'business partner', is at the wheel.

Out through Kabul's suburbs. Out into the flat landscapes surrounding Kabul. Out through a valley of huge stones which have the appearance and eeriness of meteorites.

Faruk tells us we are on the road that leads to the ruins of an ancient city by the name of Ay Khanum – The Moon Lady, an early centre of Graeco-Buddhist culture and reputed to be a 'place of power', predating by thousands of years Alexander the Great's campaign in Afghanistan. My ears prick up, interested. Faruk is obviously more educated than he looks and I love poetic history.

He continues: 'The Moon Lady was responsible for the attainment of a religious ecstasy through *rhythmic movement,*' then glances sideways at me with a vague lasciviousness. Jens laughs. I devour the landscape.

The valley narrows. We turn off along a rough track running along a ten-foot perimeter fence of serious coils of barbed wire.

'Military zone,' says Faruk.

We are going to picnic on the edge of a military zone?

'No one comes here,' he says, as if reading my mind. I see, so here it's safe for him to be with us – or is this a set-up, a CIA connection?

We stop at the edge of a small thicket. Hop out, walk around. Dappled light and a clean warm breeze play between thin trees with small, clean-green leaves. It's lovely.

But where's the food for our picnic? There's a bottle of red Russian wine.

Now what? Faruk is down on his knees in the middle of the thicket, cutting and scooping out the hard dry soil with a pocket knife. He makes a small hole, and now another about nine inches from the first. He carves a tunnel between the two; is sticking the neck of a broken wine bottle, which he's just taken out of his jacket pocket into the smaller of the holes… What?

Jens gives Faruk a paper bag of hashish. Crumbled hashish, enough to satisfy a battalion of smokers, is tipped into the earth bowl. I should have known.

Their butts are in the air, their mouths to the earth. They're taking turns at sucking at the round-lipped neck as a small bonfire of soft blue smoke rises from the earth bowl.

A small wind plays in the grasses…

Back at the Behzad; passing through the entrance way, and about to pass the shadowy figure behind the front desk.

'Message.' The gargoyle's bloodshot eyes are leering at me. Ever since the little prosecutor's attempted seduction the gargoyle has become vulturish with apparent lust. It's repulsive.

I'm careful not to touch his fingers as he hands me the piece of paper. I'm to call the consul.

'Victoria.'

'Yes.'

'The ambassador was telephoned by your aunt in Canada. He informed her that you haven't had an accident, but that you are on trial for drug smuggling. Your aunt asked the ambassador to inform you that you are not to seek any further assistance from her.'

Humiliation and sorrow. My aunt has disowned me, on the word of a stranger.

*Diary:*
*It is like the women prisoners' brief allowance of happiness once a week on Visitors' Day for, whenever I have a brief interlude of transporting thought, music and even a sense of fun it is swiftly erased by a punishing reality.*

*'Good', 'Bad' was the young servant boy's — my brother's — perception of people. But maybe this 'Good-Bad' black-white extremism is larger than human consciousness, and uses us, plays with us, taunts us; elevating only so as to reduce us.*

*Bereft, tiny splinter upon tiny splinter of identity falls. Sleep, rise, anaesthetise, fight to halt the running poison of struggling health. In mind, in sleep, no dreams to lift the heart. Forced dependence. Held.*

I phone Assilan. We arrange to meet at our usual rendezvous.

He has spoken with his father who agreed to assist. To this end his father has met with the Deputy Minister of Justice, who will also help me. For a fee. He will guarantee my freedom for $2000. My remaining sum.

He must have told his father of my financial circumstances, and his father negotiated with the Deputy Minister with this is mind.

And what about my cameras?

'It would be better if I were to speak on your behalf to the prosecutors, Victoria,' says Assilan. 'We will use the Governor's letter as our back-up authority for the return of your property. I have a two-hour break between my exams tomorrow. We will visit the prosecutors' office then, and recover your cameras.'

The office is crammed with men, some of whose faces I recognise — the prosecutors who were so determined to deny me bail during my imprisonment. I remain at a distance — by the door.

Assilan, holding the Governor's letter, steps into their midst, introduces himself — as a British Embassy translator? His manner is formal, confident. They make no attempt to call his bluff.

He reads out the Governor's letter. The prosecutors listen intently.

Now he is speaking directly to them.

Their expressions are becoming resentful, defensive. Is it his person that is arousing their ire? His physiognomy is of a different racial or tribal type to these men. But it's more than this; he has a manner which, confident in its truth, reveals the prosecutors for what they are: weak shadowy creatures who derive their sense of being through the negation of others.

A poisonous argument is erupting; the prosecutors' faces are contorted with venom. A violence of words screams from their twisted mouths. Demonically ugly, they stand, strain their bodies, collectively try to shout Assilan down.

But he's standing his ground, *ablaze* with authoritative protest. He is a modern, one against twenty traditionals; a privileged, aristocratic landowner among robotic government lackeys. What does it all mean?

They surround him, shouting. I'm on the outer rim, but abstractly involved.

The prosecutors' anger is swelling into a *hot-cold hatred*. Billowing around me…

A sensation of

*separateness*, of

*calm*.

I am so very

*tall*,

*light*.

They are *below* me, *small, inconsequential*. Their fury as naught.

A split second and I'm back, my own size again. Assilan's eyes are on me, his face, his being afire. We leave the room.

He has failed. The letter has failed. But I'm still so overwhelmed by the visitation of Divine Grace upon my being that I don't at this moment really care about this material realm.

Did I for one 'flash' meet – become – a… *pure spirit?* Or is there another face to anger: transcendent calm?

## forty-three

*Diary*
*Time… ticks… in numbers. The emotions revolve with the hours, around… and…*
*around…*

I keep myself sane by playing with clay – smooth, brown, malleable clay. To obtain it I spat on a handful of dirt and showed it to the gargoyle.

'Clay.'

He didn't know the word but he understood the substance. A small amount of cash and he obtained it for me. I now have something to occupy myself with while waiting for the Deputy Minister of Justice to fulfil his word.

It is a week since I gave Assilan the remaining $2000. We met in the coffee house three days ago for an update on my situation. It was a necessarily brief meeting as Assilan is in the thick of his exams and, understandably, can't afford to give me the attention he says he would like to.

He told me he had given the money to his father, who had in turn given it to the Deputy Minister of Justice. As a prisoner I have had to pay in advance of results. That's the system.

The Deputy Minister is now, according to Assilan, collaborating with the Court of Appeal judges about me. However, before a retrial can be set the file has to be processed by 'the clerks': the clerks in the prison compound's judicial area, then the clerks working in the Ministry of Justice. The Deputy Minister has ordered that the file be processed 'swiftly'.

So, in the knowledge that my sovereign individuality is currently shackled to the government's faceless underlings I have turned to clay. I have also acquired a box of watercolour paints and two fine-tipped paintbrushes. My room is my studio.

Mess, clay-fingered ooze, absorption…

Days – a week? – later, four infant gargoyles emerge from the cook's oven. Each has four faces, looking in every direction so they can't be tricked.

Delicately, ferociously, wizardly, I paint my quadruplet of defenders, who then take up residence on my bedside table. Fighting for my freedom.

Another week has gone by and I feel a familiar desperation mounting. I *need* to leave this country today, this hour, this minute. *What* is going on?

Another rendezvous with Assilan. He is troubled. I see it as soon as I reach the top of the stairs and look toward our table.

The file has, *thank goodness*, been processed by the prison compound clerks and was sent to the Ministry of Justice five days ago. But it has not been seen since – is lost somewhere in the six-storey building.

Lost? My file *lost*?

I had never felt it before but now I do. Doubt. A dreadful doubt. Have I been deceived by this man? Until now I have trusted him implicitly. He is Assilan, my saviour, my animus, working behind the scenes for my deliverance from the 'justice' of Afghanistan. Or is he?

As I sit over my coffee my thoughts run amok.

It was Assilan who gave me the drug that made me stupefied and numb when I was due to fly out of Afghanistan. He who took my $1000 and paid it to the judge of the Court of Narcotics. Or said he had. He who took my last $2000 and *supposedly* gave it to his father, who *supposedly* gave it to the Deputy Minister of Justice. So why haven't I been released?

And worst of all, if I have been set up, was it a sly and clever Assilan and not the Police Minister who organised with the CIA and customs to trap me at the airport?

He breaks into my thoughts. 'I am very sorry for the worry this delay is causing you.' There is sincerity in his voice, concern. A splash of sadness in his eyes…

Torn.

*The fire burns. Love speaks in his voice – my saviour or murderer? The one I trust to set me free, Assilan, Lion Man which do you be?*

## forty-four

Whether it is because the pressure of his exams is almost over, or because he senses my doubt, Assilan has arranged that we meet every day at the coffee house so that he can tell me of any developments.

But there is another reason; there's an intangible sense of urgency, beyond my fragile trust.

Every meeting to date has brought a further apology, and I have no expectations for this afternoon's rendezvous.

A *breakthrough!* Assilan has heard word that the file is somewhere between the first and fourth floors of the Ministry of Justice building.

Excited, forgetting that we shouldn't be seen together in public, we jump into a taxi.

Fifteen minutes later we're out in the countryside, stopping at the entrance of a monolithic grey-white Ministry of Justice building. I'm to accompany Assilan in the search.

We are confronted by a maze of corridors, offices, and the blank intransigence of their occupants: an overpopulation of white shirts, black jackets and black heads sitting at desks.

Nothing on the firstsecondthird floor.

On each floor I have waited in the corridor as Assilan combed the rooms, questioning, questioning.

Perspiration is running on his brow, from the physical exertion of politely interrogating the hundreds of clean-shaven, smug, reluctant, Brylcreemed clerks. So far, to no avail.

We pad our way up the otherwise empty stairs toward the fourth floor. I hear his breath, soft and even. With every step inhaling, exhaling, in unison with mine… inhaling exhaling… igniting a fire in my heart – a *heart-rush* of love for this man, his goodness. Consuming all and every doubt.

We reach the fourth floor and walk along a stone corridor. At the very end there is an entrance to a vast room. I look in. There must be 500 clerks in there. Assilan motions to me to wait outside.

He is moving with authority from one clerk to another, to another, another… twenty, fifty… He's pausing longer than he did with the others. Something is happening, I can see by his body language: *he's found it!*

Assilan is at my side. 'That clerk has your file; he has been holding it all this time. He wanted a bribe. I told him that he will be imprisoned if he doesn't hand it over. We will have it in ten minutes.'

His relief is tangible. A lightening in both of us.

We wait in the stone corridor, which has an open balcony overlooking the building's main entrance. We stand, leaning against the balcony looking down to the courtyard. Until my impatience gets the better of me.

'The clerk, what's the clerk doing?'

I move toward the doorway, looking into the room, implying to a clerk in the distance to get a move on.

'Sissssss!'

Assilan is *sissing* at me. I'm shocked by it: it's not a sound I link to him. He's beckoning to me to come quickly. I'm in time to see why. Soldiers, down in the courtyard near the main entrance. And four men, handcuffed, surrounded, being led into the Supreme Court Chambers.

'Taraki, that one in the middle, you see?' Assilan is very agitated. 'He is the leader of the Socialist Party. The others are also members. Just two days ago Daoud's secret police killed two others.'

I don't understand. 'What is the Socialist Party?' I ask, needing to know why he is so agitated.

Assilan is about to say something when he glances toward the clerk's office, stops. No, he is not going to explain. Too public?

My file is enormous, as if every clerk in Kabul has added his life's story to it; an indecipherable lovely-looking script of blue-ink circles, squares and oblongs of various governmental stamps. Plus, at the back, eight pages of Jens' and my fingerprints. It has the appearance of a sacred text.

We're in the back seat of the taxi, driving back to Kabul, to the prison compound. Assilan is so silent and tense.

'Why were those men arrested?' I ask him tactfully, aware that something momentous has occurred. A sharp, surreptitious movement of his hand stops me talking. I understand. Taxi drivers are not mere taxi drivers here; clerks not just clerks. And they sometimes understand English.

Assilan knows where in the prison compound to deliver my file, knows the Court of Appeal rooms. I wait as he hurries in with my file. And hurries back out. It's been delivered.

'You are to meet with the judges tomorrow at 11am. Just a meeting, not a trial. I will meet you at the coffee house at midday.'

Distracted, he hurries away.

## forty-five

The room, a sombre elegance of dark polished timbers, feels cool to me in my cotton dress. Deep purple velvet curtains are drawn across a wall of windows.

Ahead of me a composed figure sits cross-legged on a prayer mat on a wooden raised platform, staring.

I walk toward the judge, a silken scarf wrapped about my head, my eyes to the wooden floor. I stop a short distance from him. Unafraid, look up.

His eyes are serene, kindly-looking. I bow my head in respect and greeting. He replies similarly.

To my right, three more judges sit cross-legged on a mat on the floor, their turbans and flowing robes richly coloured and elaborate; Rubenesque.

They are still as statues, studying me. I nod my head. They reply in kind, gesture to me to sit with them.

It's awkward for me to cross my legs, almost embarrassing.

Lifting their eyes, they greet me: 'Salaam.'

'Salaam,' I reply. It means peace.

A hairless, bejewelled male hand reaches out and grasps the arm of a tall-stemmed, elegantly rounded silver urn on a silver tray in the centre of our circle. There are cinnamon cakes, dates and petite almond biscuits as well. The judge to my left inclines his head, smiles and pours me a glass of tea. Gestures to me to partake of the condiments. How *gracious*.

The judges shift their attention, fall into conversation among themselves.

I take a sip; *mmm...* cardamom flavoured.

The judges include me in their conversation by way of periodic friendly-fatherly glances. A sense of ease filters through me. As impossible as it seems, I am enjoying sitting here with the three judges, listening to the soothing musical tones of the Persian language and quietly studying them.

Large red rubies and other precious stones are set in engraved silver rings on their fingers, their nails are sculptured, their hands fine. Long, thick, curled black beards reach munificently down their dark-blue, brown, deep-red and purple robes. Their speech and movements are measured and mannerly.

How refined and aristocratic they are – the holders of my fate. Indisputably patriarchs of the old world, biblically magnificent.

A voice speaks from behind me. The judge on the platform is saying something to the three, is concluding our tea party. I am to stand and approach him.

'In two days' time, as tomorrow is our holiday, you are to come for your release papers.' He nods his head – affirming that my freedom is guaranteed?

Now he looks to the others, who, in the manner of self-assured old men, are smiling at me. Are gently nodding their confirmation of my imminent release.

I bow and leave the judges' room.

*Euphoric.*

Outside it is bright, hot – dusty-hot. I amble through the prison compound toward the prison gate.

The young soldier in the sentry box catches my eye. One arm is raised and bent to provide a cushion for his face, the other lazily nursing the rifle leaning against his thigh, his boots unlaced, his rough woven jacket unbuttoned. Relaxed, young and harmless-looking, the gun in his hand a charade.

It's only 11.35am. Half an hour until my rendezvous with Assilan. I dawdle through the streets, peering into antique shops, studying the Persian carpets antiquing out on the roads, courtesy of the city's traffic. I pretend I'm interested in buying 'that carpet hanging there', 'there', 'there', just for the fun of it. No 'free', 'free'. The merchants no longer intimidate me.

I arrive early at the coffee house: excited, eager to tell Assilan my news. Eager to express to him my Everlasting Gratitude.

At midday, footsteps on the stairs and here he is – this truly princely man. But he's looking distant, almost as if he's not registering where he is.

My good news is received with relief, for my sake and as proof that his word has been honoured, yet his voice is constrained and he's ill at ease. It has something do with what we witnessed at the Ministry of Justice yesterday.

It's safe here; he trusts, confides in me: 'With the arrest of Taraki, the underground leader, all hope for democracy for Afghanistan has been crushed. The Socialist Party will be disbanded, its known members shot. We intellectuals and students will be harassed and arrested. The dictatorship will continue. It is a very bad situation for the people of Afghanistan.'

Politics, democracy, history, his country. I know so very little about any of it, absorbed as I have been in my own traumatic experiences. I'm embarrassed at my ignorance. My first humble question: 'What is the dictatorship?'

'President Douad is the dictator of my country. You will have seen large posters of him as you travelled through Afghanistan.'

I remember seeing these posters: thirty-foot-high portraits of a bald man wearing sunglasses and a dour expression. They were posted throughout the landscapes I travelled across and at the time I wondered why this dull face held such prominence.

'Daoud is cousin of the King of Afghanistan. (Afghanistan has a king?) He married the King's sister before overthrowing him and sending him into exile, thus disrupting the 200 years of peace.'

Seeing my confusion Assilan continues. 'I shall tell you a little of my country's history, Victoria. So that you may understand.'

Assilan settles back in his chair. This is going to take time.

Afghanistan consists mainly of tribes, Assilan begins. The Pathans, the Mohmands, Mangals, Waziris, Tajiks, Uzbeks, Hazaras and many more. These tribes have their ethnic origins in Greece, Persia, Mongolia, India, Russia, Turkey and date back to ancient times, when Afghanistan was not a nation but a passageway for wave upon wave of conquerors: from Alexander the Great, the Scythian and Turkish invaders, the White Huns, to Genghis Khan, the Timurids. And many more. Historically these tribes, and their warlords and chiefs, were unable to co-exist peaceably unless united by a war against invaders.

He leans forward, his hands resting on our table. Continues.

'This was the situation until the year 1747. Then a change took place. Afghanistan's people linked together as an army of tribes under an internally founded kingdom, the one from which King Muhammad Zahir Shah is descended. Part of the success of 200 years of internal peace was a royal decree enshrining freedom and dignity for the individual. But these rights vanished when Daoud seized power.'

At the mention of this name Assilan, this most gentle of gentle men, is suddenly rigid… silent… his anger visibly rising. It's a controlled, white-hot furnace of anger.

I daren't speak. I look at his hands. He's pressing his palms so hard against the table-top that the blood has withdrawn from his fingers.

His voice is quiet, steely with resolve: 'I will raise my people; I will raise an army of 70,000. Together we will destroy the dictatorship of Daoud.' His body is rigid with determination, his voice, his being, so tight, unhappy.

I feel a maternal urge to comfort. 'But you study medicine to save life, not destroy it. You once told me it was your ambition to serve humanity. Revolution – a bloody revolution – is surely the antithesis of everything you believe in?'

No reply.

'There *is* another way. Killing and maiming is not the way. That is for fools.'

'Fools – a fool controls Afghanistan now.' Assilan does not lift his eyes and his features are folded, darkened by a wall of anger that will not allow him to see reason, or recognise me.

'There is another way.' I'm as stubborn as he in my perception, although I can't quite fathom what this 'other way' might be.

Stalemate. I cannot penetrate. His maleness will not allow me to awaken him to the refined, compassionate person that he is, and to whom I owe *infinite* gratitude. At this moment he cannot see me. He is as a stranger to me, a lord of the land intent on vengeance.

So be it. Afghanistan's politics have nothing to do with me, and in two days' time I'm to be finally freed from here.

Assilan and I leave together, turning to walk in opposite directions – one carrying love, the other anger. We will speak again in a day or two.

## forty-six

I've obtained a pot of tea, opened my French doors, slipped off my dress and put on light pants and T-shirt. I've put my chair outside, placing it so that my back is to the sun.

An early summer's day; the yellow heat is beating down. A strong not unpleasant smell of hay dust and horse permeates the dry windless air. I roll my pants up to my knees.

The grey-white mare, just a few feet away, snorts. Is lifting one hoof. Clunks it down metallically. She is uncomfortable in this heat. She won't look at me. She has never looked at me.

The sun sinks deliciously into my shoulders. *So relaxed*. No more fear or threat of imprisonment.

Perspiration forms. *Good*. It will help to rid my body of its toxins. Beads of perspiration trickle down my chest, thighs, calves, through my hair, my forehead, down my face. Little tickling rivulets trace their way down my body.

Suddenly a decidedly different sensation, on my legs. Tickling *up* my legs, like hundreds of little feet – ants! Large black ants! An *army* of large black ants is trailing in single file along the concrete and up my legs. They must have sensed the moisture running down my body and are climbing me to have a drink. They're not biting, and as long as they don't climb too high they're quite welcome to drink me…

Daydreaming: I am free, far away from those who sought to imprison my body with their lusts and laws, drifting, dreamily, amidst flashing blue seas, green leaves, wafting, lazily. On a carpet of golden sands, on a South Pacific island. Blue seas, green leaves, golden sandzzz … dream-ily… drift-ing… warmmm…

A distant rumble. Summer thunder?

Boom! Boom! Dynamite. There must be a quarry somewhere on the outskirts of the city.

Booom! Booom! Booom!

No, that's not dynamite. It sounds like the volleys fired back home on the Queen's birthday. Home… I'll soon be home. Fortressed by the ocean: remoteness, delicious solitude.

More booms. I wonder what they're celebrating?

And here, slouching around the corner of the hotel, comes that increasingly unpleasant servant boy. The surly slime, he thinks I'm a whore, has behaved almost aggressively toward me ever since that prosecutor's visit. He bends down to pick up the tray and the empty teapot. Boom! Boom! Boom! Obviously, unless he's deaf, we've both heard those distant sounds.

'Celebration?' I smile at him, as I refuse to let his distorted thoughts affect me. He ignores me. Maybe he doesn't know this English word. Try again: 'Celebration?' Same smile, but just a little bit more vehement.

'No. No celebration. *Revolution!*'

He *spat* that at me. Now he's slouching back around the corner. Scuff, scuff, scuff – even the way he walks is sub.

He's lying, surely! But those last booms did sound a little closer than the earlier ones. And I think they came from a different direction.

Booom! Booom! *Boooom* That last one was not far from *here*.

It's 1.30pm. Why am I looking at my watch?

Guns, big guns, are firing now from different directions. *In* the city.

A rumbling crunching metallic sound. Something large moving along the street. I get up, go to the gate. Two of the Danish girls, weeping, panic-stricken, rush past me into the hotel.

'An armoured tank!' I say out loud, in disbelief. It's about 200 yards away, at the end of the street. It's reversing, rumbling toward me… passing me.

The half torso of the soldier protruding stiffly from the top of the tank with one arm bent into a clean triangle in a sort of salute looks as if he is made of the same metal as the machine, looks as if he is welded on. I *have* to photograph him. Camera. One of the Danish tourists, a new friend of Jens', has one. I dash back into the hotel.

They've all gathered, Jens and the tourists, near the hotel kitchen. They're listening to the two ashen-faced girls. Something traumatic has occurred.

I don't understand Danish but Jens fills me in. The girls have just come from the centre of Kabul where fighting has broken out. A tank had run over a paraplegic beggar – they saw him being cut in half. Then as they were fleeing down a backstreet they were caught in crossfire and watched helplessly as a child ran out into the road and straight into a spray of machine-gun bullets.

I picture the horror of what they witnessed, but it's abstract, as if I'm reading it in a newspaper. Foremost in my mind is the image of the tank and its sighter. '*I need* a camera. *Now!*' Jens gets one for me and I dash back to the street.

The tank is now at the other end of the street but is turning, rumbling toward me. A quick glance around me: all the shops are closed, barricaded. And there, to my left, at the intersection with one of the city's main thoroughfares, an exodus of people fleeing the city, ranks of soldiers directing them. My street has been blocked. There is no way out.

The tank and me – that's all that's in the street.

It's coming toward me, rumbling, cutting the tarmac. I'm on the footpath, camera ready. It's about to pass. Tank and man in frame, focused, hold breath…

What? *Shock!* A hand! A large hairy white hand is clamped on my wrist.

'Take one photograph and you will be shot.' It's a Russian accent. Two men, one on either side of me, white-skinned, large. God only knows where they've sprung from. The street was empty.

It all happens so fast. The servant, closing the hotel's gates, sees me, comes toward me… grabs the camera strap. He's pulling at it, trying to take it, to smash it. He's scared out of his wits; angry.

I'm holding on. It's not my camera. 'No photo, no photo!' I shout, fired with surprise. The hairy white hand releases its grip on my wrist. The servant pulls me fiercely by the camera strap, inside.

He lets go as he bolts the ten-foot hotel gates. We're closed in. I'm stunned, motionless.

I look up and out – up to that permanent-thin blue sky, a hill beneath it which I recognise. It was covered in snow when I first arrived in Kabul. The snow has long gone.

But what is that? Moving toward-above the hill?

A cloud, an enormous heavy grey cloud is moving above the hill. But there has not been a single hint of a cloud for two months or more. It is sky-rolling angrily toward the city, a vast shadow… *swallowing the hill.*

The hill. It is also *moving*, seething with the brown-grey of thousands of ant-sized soldiers. Camouflaged by that huge cloud they're pouring down the hill toward the city. *In my direction.*

Hot electric shiver; *fear.* Get into the hotel fast.

Machine-gun fire all around, sounding through the walls.

I know the safest place is in this otherwise crumbling hotel, which is so decayed it wouldn't withstand much more than a hefty kick. I head for the passageway between the kitchen and the guest rooms.

I'm not alone in this thinking. They're all here, the Danish tourists, huddling together with blankets and pillows. They look terrified. What a contrast with their usual aloof, casual confidence.

They have claimed the strongest wall, the one furthest from the street. What do I do? Stand, *here*.

## forty-seven

Closed in by walls, fear, the sounds of an opening-growing-encompassing – *war*?

A long whistling-whining is heading this way. It's a *bomb*… A malevolent silence…

*K… pooomph!*

Shattering. Everything sh-a-k-e-s, *shaking*. Whimpering, crying, the Danes clutch one another, their heads in their chests.

Another; whistling-whining… silence… *Boooooom!* Tanks out on the street are open-firing now.

*K… pooomph!*

F-F-F-Flakes of pastel… *Boooooom!* Blue stucco f-falling – *Boooooom!* – like snow.

The Danes are panicking – feeding one another's terror through their collective embrace, feeding that thought: *we are going to die.*

I stand apart; just that measure of distance to save me from succumbing to the contagion: their abject terror.

*Retreat, retreat to my room.*

Alone.

The French doors – they're open! Closed. I sit on my bed. This is *unbelievable*, an unbelievably *bad dream*. My mind flashes back to the young soldier at the prison gate. I had tried to imagine how his innocent, gentle face would turn if he had to use his gun to kill. But I couldn't imagine such a transformation. And that was only – what? – a couple of hours ago!

*Boooooom!*

Stay sitting on your bed, I tell myself, watching the flakes of pastel wall fall. Another whining-whistling… *silence…*

Is it going to explode on…

*K… pooomph!*

Brittle bones hot fear blood surging, *pumping.* It didn't hit.

Outside. Tanks: crunching wheels, tracking backwards-forwards. *Boooooom! Boooooom!* Staccato bursts of machine-guns, creeping soldiers. Where are they?

*Boooooom!* Rat-a-tat-tat-tat-tat! *Whistle… K… pooomph!*

I've heard all of these horrifying sounds before. In lazy Sunday afternoon TV wartime romances, with dashing heroes and sultry goddesses sucking seductively on long cigarette holders: Lauren Bacall, Greta Garbo, Marlene Dietrich, Bette Davis, Katharine Hepburn…

A murky grey soup has swallowed the sun, has…

*Boooooom! Whistle… K… pooomph!*

…sucked the summer light from this room.

It is the *sounds* of war that are so terrifying. I had never known this before.

Perfectly still. Powerless. Sitting in the middle of my bed. My feet are on the shaking floor. Mind racing: run, jump, hide, escape?

Night. Blackness. *Nightmare*
> S
> C
> R
> E
> A
> M

ripping through the night, through the roof, into my head.

A jet, bomber, *descending.*

*Whuuuuuumph!*

The air's *imploding.*

I'm on the floor, my fingers scrabbling like a trapped rat's claws… clawing my way under my tiny bed… to the corner walls. Foetal. My body out of control with terror, my heart thumping thumping thumping thumping in my bursting ears…

Hour

upon hour

upon merciless hour the

*Screaming*, bombs, roars, blasts, tearing-teeth-of-war scrape-scraping at the streets the walls at my convulsively shaking foetal flesh, my thumping-heart-in-head and tiny life. Waiting… for what? For what?

*If you are to die, die in peace.*

A voice, *inside* my head.

My body immediately obeys, is relaxing, unwinding. My heart is… slowing. My body… wriggling out from underneath my bed, climbing on top.

Sleeping.

Grey light filtering into my room. Dawn. The bombing, the war, it's more distant but still alive. I'm still alive. Leaden-chested, too scared to move.

Lie still.

Am feeling so hollow.

A yearning arises in me. A need for human comfort, to be with others. I get up and go out into the passageway.

The tourists are in the same positions I had left them yesterday afternoon. Fear and sleeplessness have embalmed them in a motionless huddle. Their eyes are glassy, vacant. They are catatonic with shock.

They may as well be dead, and I need *life*… I walk out onto the porch and sit opposite the gargoyle's habitual perch. I feel so weak, hammered, mashed.

The light is diffused, mist-drizzly. Green; a small patch of thin green grass. It wasn't there yesterday.

Droplets of rain fall from the branches of the large tree. It is the first rain for more than two months. Drop, drop, drop. Like tears.

A sound, like large teeth scraping the ground. A familiar munching sound. Nibble by nibble, blade by blade. Her mouth, her large yellow teeth, the skin of her gums, her wide nostrils. Nibble by nibble, blade by blade, slowly she comes into view. Her eyes are down, concentrating on the tiny blades of new grass. The profile of her grey-white head;

her strong neck. Her rope has frayed, is broken.

She doesn't know I'm watching her. How sad, how terribly sad she looks. Can an animal feel such a sadness as I see in her? She lifts her eye. Looks straight *into* mine, caught unawares. She swiftly pulls back. Traumatised.

The tourists stir, disentangling themselves, talking in little voices. I pass through them and into the hotel kitchen.

Noise: spitting, cracking. A male voice and loud frenetic hissing. A circle of backs: the gargoyle, the cook, his wife and the servant boy are clustered around a radio.

The gargoyle looks around at me. Bloodshot eyes wide, he rasps: 'President Douad killed, government *finis*. Revolution success.'

I need a glass of tea, some nan or something to eat.

I see the child, the cook's little girl. She has been hurt. She sits upright, her legs dangling over the edge of her bunk, numbly staring down at her parents. Her head is wrapped in a bloodied makeshift bandage. Wet red blood.

The gargoyle notices me looking at her. 'Bomb. No hospital. Dangerous.'

I hope she's going to be okay.

The hours pass… the punching 'Booooms' recede into distant… muffled… slow… silence.

As the news continues to blare through the cook's radio, a little more and a little bit more as the day deepens, the bomber jets, although no longer dive-bombing fifty feet above the hotel, continue to scream-spiral, rise-dive-rip the sky…

The palace, only half a mile away from the Behzad, has been bombed. President Daoud, is, according to the gargoyle, dead. He had continued to refuse to sign his government over to the revolutionaries as each member of his family was shot before his eyes.

The gargoyle's nicotine-breath sprays me. 'Finished. New Democratic Republic of Afghanistan victorious.'

He's thrilled. Is it victory over the dictator, his oppressive omnipotence – the ego's *fake* omnipotence, paid for in the deaths of his entire family and himself that so excites him? Or is it the victors' cruelty?

A liquid sorrow, that of a woman's voice, arises in my heart. It is a memory – the emotional memory of Mahler's *The Song of the Earth*. The profound melancholy of the sixth song, 'The Farewell'.

# forty-eight

It is the morning of the fourth day after the revolution.

Trapped inside the hotel. Locked in, trapped inside shock, fear and an unabating insecurity. The past few days are a blank, I cannot remember them. Lost to future nightmares?

The Scandinavian tourists, particularly the women, are in a state of nervous collapse: loud, semi-hysterical, their eyes wide-staring and unfocused; the foundations of their illusory normality obliterated.

Outside: for a breath of air. The sky has returned to normal – a pale blue filled with the yellow heat of early summer.

But it is not quite normal. High in the upper atmosphere the military jets – a criss-cross of silver streaks upon the blue – continue their thin-piercing and threatening presence.

I walk around to the front of the hotel and notice that the gates are open. I can see the street. Does this mean we are free to walk about?

'Gate close 2pm. Curfew.' The gargoyle has returned to his perch, his concrete ledge lookout.

It's 10am. I want to walk about, to offload the tension, and see what state the city is in. But not alone. I go back inside, and into the hotel restaurant to look for Jens. He's not there. The others are – they've taken over the restaurant.

I find Jens in his room, mindless, drug-numbed. I suggest that we take a look at the city. He's willing.

The first thing I feel is the changed atmosphere: the air is heavy, oppressive. All is tense, silent. No one has reopened their shops. Nobody is about. The streets are ripped, gouged with tank marks, bomb craters. There are bomb-shattered walls, machine-gun-fire patterns wherever I look.

Soldiers are scattered about, on sentry duty in the street we have just entered. They look so aggressive, *murderous*. We shrink past them, pretending we're just moving litter… rubble.

The streets begin to widen. Though not consciously intending to, we are heading toward the city centre.

A small gathering of peasant-civilians is placing a wreath of flowers on the gun barrel of an immobilised tank. And scattering bags of flower petals over it. Their smiles look false, masking their fear.

At the edge of the city centre, not far from the palace, bombarded buildings strain brokenly against the sky; their broken shapes a jagged anarchy in the place of what recently were ugly-white conformist squares of architecture.

Obedience and authority have been reduced to ghostliness. A strange pleasure – a wildness – awakens in my veins.

Although we don't hear them, we abruptly come upon a sea of tribal men filling an area of the city's centre. There must be a couple of thousand of them.

Jens and I seem to know instinctively that we should not approach. We stop in our tracks.

The crowd is tightly packed, bonded – by fear and uncertainty? – their faces slightly uplifted as if scenting the air. The atmosphere is expectant – a surreal, animal expectancy. I immediately recognise it. It belongs to my dream of the Khyber Pass.

Jens and I do not belong here. We turn and hurry back to the hotel.

Here, almost reeling with the surety, I scribble in my diary:

*Diary:*
*Does a dream 'create' a reality to come, or merely hint at it? Either way, prophetic vision confirms the existence of the unimaginable; a seeing of, yet larger than self!*
*There will be a terrible war within this area of the world.*

In the meantime I need a glass of tea.

In the kitchen the bloodied bandage wrapping the little girl's head wound has been replaced by a clean white one and she looks considerably happier. The cook must have taken his daughter to hospital while Jens and I were out in the city.

I like the cook and his family. Stocky and rotund, they are polite, and despite the forgotten-unforgotten terror of recent days are *cheerful*, and ever ready to oblige. They are busy kneading dough for nan, cutting up vegetables, cooking and preparing food.

I much prefer to be in here with them than in the hotel lounge, which has been taken over by the Scandinavians and turned into a centre for collective neurosis.

But their distress is understandable. No one is able to leave this city, this country. Or, as Jens and I discovered earlier, even safely leave the hotel.

The borders are closed, the airport is closed.

The telecommunication systems are destroyed.

## forty-nine

*Diary:*

*Suspended time, suspended thought, suspended life.*

*We are all prisoners. All numbed. All trapped in a fear of a war-beast brute-slinking inexorably closer.*

*Hatred – the psychotic Cyclops rears in the heart of Man. Not so in the heart of the artist-poet-mystic. Madness: an absurd hope that amid this political chaos I might be able to slip through the bureaucratic net. It is like a coating of optimism protecting my sanity, allowing me to gather together the broken pieces of my reality.*

*What was – is – my reality?*

*What has happened to the judges of the Court of Appeal? The Deputy Minister of Justice? My trial? The last of my money – the bought promise of my freedom? And, dare I wonder: Assilan?*

*No think. I must concentrate on this moment, this 'now'…*

I put down my pen, regain my focus…

A host of little faces is before me. My children! My little clay defenders! I have neglected you – have forgotten our morning ritual of turning you around, of acknowledging each and every one of your sixteen wee sharp-eyed faces. You are covered in the dust of war.

I pick up each one and blow away the dulling dust. Breathe new life into them. Turn their multiple personalities around.

There. I have soothed them. Soothed the troubled ground on which we all stand.

Now what? Where *do* I stand?

I reach for my suitcase and search out my air ticket. Reading the fine print I see that I have just *twelve days* before the ticket becomes invalid – is worthless. *Twelve days* to get on a plane out of here.

I have one $100 bill left. That's all.

I will not *panic*.

Assilan. The revolution is now a week old. Are you alive? *Please be alive.*

On the eighth day after the revolution comes good news. The borders and the airport have reopened. *All foreigners are required to leave forthwith.* The new government has ordered us all to get out.

The phones are working again. I can ring the British consul.

'Can I leave?' I ask him.

'No. Not without your passport. Not without the official release papers.'

I'm gutted. It's too dangerous for me to go anywhere near the judicial zone.

But even if I could they won't let me go. How absurd to have thought that I could slip through the net. I catch the gargoyle looking at me from behind the register, trying to read me.

> *Diary:*
>
> *It is as if I have been – am being – attacked by a huge External Negativity, an evil hungering for my destruction. Does it dwell within this pristine land? Come from the blood of the slain – of the massacres of the Ages? Blood for blood, unblessed. Unending?*
>     *Mother of God, Mother of kindness: get me out of here, please get me out of here.*

Outside my door I can hear the tourists, their inertia and tension falling from them like a cloak, flurry heavy-footed through the passageway, talking excitedly.

Jens is also free to go home. I find this extremely difficult to accept.

Two hours go by.

I can't stand it.

I telephone the consul again, rail at him about the corruption, the bribes I have had to pay. Tell him that there is no system of justice. That I am going to expose this.

'You will never get out of this country if you do, Victoria.'

I hear the warning in his voice, back down. I know he is right.

I don't look up to see if the gargoyle is watching me from across the register desk. I know he is.

In my room I write a prayer I need to believe in:

*Diary:*
*It is only through the power of love, I know, beseech; take me from this 'prison'.*

Early afternoon. A tap on the door.

I don't know how he found out. Maybe the consul told him. A journalist, an American working for *Time* magazine, is standing at my door, telling me he's heard that I am a prisoner. Could he have a chat? He breezes in.

All I can find to say to him is: 'At the height of the war a voice inside my head said, if you are to die, die in peace!'

It's not newsworthy.

# fifty

Day nine. Jens is still here but is flying out in three days' time. The rest of the hotel is almost empty.

Jens bought his ticket this morning but he's not too fussed about going back to his homeland. He's discovered a source of opium and is indulging himself while he has the opportunity.

Assilan occupies my thoughts. I believe he is alive. *Must believe* that he is. Just keep waiting, I tell myself. As if I have a choice.

But there *is* a choice, which is revealed to me while I am sitting on my chair outside my French doors, The gargoyle has come to brush and tend to the mare, now retethered in her corner close to my door.

As he approaches me I can see that he has had an idea. His guttural rasp: 'Peshawar, no passport okay.' His bloodshot eyes have widened. He shoots a glance back to the horse, to me.

'Me know passage through mountains. You ride her – his fingers stab his chest – I take you. Peshawar. Five-six days maybe. You, Muslim woman.'

Presumably he means that I am to disguise myself beneath a burka. It is not a stupid idea.

If Assilan does not contact me very soon I will allow the lustful gargoyle to assist me to escape. It would be better to face the dangers inherent in that plan than remain here, where I surely will not survive. But what will this cost me?

Day ten, and ten days until my ticket expires.

Find diversions. Go to the hotel lounge, see if there are any books left behind by the tourists.

There is one: Nietzsche's *Also Sprach Zarathustra*, the German edition. Wasn't Zarathustra a Persian? And a protagonist of the concept of good and evil, the *triumph* of light over darkness?

There is a folded slip of paper in the back. An English translation…

'That soul that best loveth itself, in which all things have their ebb and flow and counterflow – oh how should that highest soul not have the vilest parasites…'
I think I need a pot of tea.

And another pot of tea. I have an unquenchable thirst; anxiety. The words *Please let me know you're alive* are engraved on my every breath.

It's lunchtime. A daily plateful of rice, a bowl of yogurt, and enough raw garlic to punch the lights out of the amoebas in my gut.

I take my lunch in the hotel kitchen, savouring the homely smell of roasting nan and the comforting simplicity of the cook, his wife and their head-healing child as I eat.

Lunch finished, I put the kettle on the gas burner to make a pot of tea to take to my room. Normally the servant boy brews and delivers tea but I enjoy having a task to do.

Sleeping… waking. Staring at the ceiling, at the cracks and gaps formed during the bombing. They're pathways. Crooked, erratic map-tracks for the mind.

The late afternoon sun slips in, all frilly and soft, creeping across the wall, the cracks; light cracks, into black cracks.

It's edging toward 9pm. The kitchen will close in a few minutes. There is just enough time for *one more* pot of tea.

The servant boy is in his kitchen corner spot, looking dejected. Is he missing the tourists, the busyness? And why am I feeling sorry for him; going up to him and asking him if he would make me 'a pot of chai' (tea)? Is it myself I see reflected in his face?

He nods that he will do so, and bring it to me in my room. At last, a sense of (delicate) truce between us.

The servant boy may take up to twenty minutes to prepare the tea – to boil the water, muddle about. He is always slow.

I dig out my diary and open it on the page with the pen drawing of the octopus bird that I began in Kabul Prison. I've been filling it in with gold-leaf paint from a pot under the cabinet beside my bed. I bend down to pick it up, opening the lid onto liquid gold…

*Scuff-tap.* An odd sound. On my French doors. A scuffing-tapping sound.

Again, *louder, more urgent*. A *rush* of adrenalin. *Is it?*

I leap across the room, pull back the curtain, open the doors…

*Assilan!* Standing right next to me, silently acknowledging me – his eyes bespeaking danger, haste.

He is very tense. He has crossed the city on foot. Broken the curfew to find me. He sinks into the chair. He looks exhausted.

'Politically my country has been kidnapped. The people, the supporters of the underground Socialist Party, have been deceived. It is not a democratic republic as the radio says. Daoud's fighter pilots were Russian communists – the military jets were communist Russia's.

'At first the rebel army – the land forces fighting against Daoud to return Afghanistan to the people – were winning. Then Daoud called in what he had thought was his air force, but they were not his. Instead of only attacking the rebel army, they also turned against Daoud. They bombed the palace, and then killed Daoud and his family. The Soviet Union manipulated the confrontation, and has taken control of Afghanistan.'

Assilan is suffering. Immeasurably. But, *thank the heavens*, he is alive.

'My father has disappeared – we have not seen or heard from him for the past ten days. The Deputy Minister of Justice is dead and many of the university professors and academics have been killed. The new Democratic Republic of Afghanistan is a trick, a way to deceive the people and blind them to the truth that Afghanistan has been taken. The situation is very dangerous and it is a very sad time for me and for my country…'

His father missing? Murdered? I don't know what to say. How to comfort.

I'm diverting, telling Assilan about my dream of war, of my feeling that it is somehow prophetic. Of how I turned and faced the other way.

I am almost taken aback at his response. His eyes are alert, as though in search of or connecting to something.

Now looking at me; sober, aware: 'Russia is to the north-west of Kabul, the direction you faced in your dream, Victoria.'

Our eyes minds lock, held in a frisson of recognition, suprapersonal knowing. Speechless.

Assilan shifts, gazes beyond me, his eyes lowered, his voice subdued. 'Although everything is lost, it will now be through God's help that I will see you freed from my country.'

A hussshh of waves upon my soul… I am bowed with, in…

O such nobility. He who has just lost his father, and his country, still holds to his honour, his promise to me.

The door opens. No knock. It's the servant boy, bringing in a tray with my pot of tea. Cutting in front of me, his eyes focus on and narrow with enmity toward Assilan. He puts the tray on the table, head down, leaves.

Hatred, what a festering hatred owns that youth. It hangs – freezes the air, us.

Assilan had not met the youth's eyes but now he's on his feet. Senses danger. He's at the French doors, hastening so as to get through the city before the alarm is raised. Whispering: 'The night after tomorrow.'

## fifty-one

Three soldiers have appeared from around the hotel corner. Jens and I are in the back yard sharing a morning glass of tea. I have only just got up. Ten minutes of wakefulness, no more than this.

They've stopped. Are staring at us.

One walks forward. 'Come!' is all he says. He's saying it to me. Am I being arrested?

I sit between two of them in a taxi, thinking: Perhaps Assilan has arranged this? Perhaps I'm being taken to receive my release papers and passport?

We are at the gates to the prison compound. Dismounting. Two soldiers in front, one behind me, escorting me into a building I know.

One or two of the older men in here were polite to me during my toing and froing to recover my freedom. I look but can't see them. Now there are youths behind the desks previously occupied by the older men. Where have they gone?

I'm being taken into a small courtroom.

A surprise: one judge, a *woman*, very stuffily middle class and brusque.

'You are to visit the prison for one day and one night, as your second trial is to be held tomorrow.'

My *second* trial? I cannot believe it. 'Why,' I reason, 'should I have to go to prison *before* a trial?'

'You are to visit the prison for one night…' She's not human, she's an automaton.

The soldiers lead me back through the rows of illiterate youths sitting pen-twiddling outside. Like these ignorant-looking creatures, that woman is a prop, part of the scenario covering up for the systematic murders of Afghanistan's educated and elite.

Stinking heat. A deserted buzz of static. Metallic noise.

Descending the steps to the mud courtyard and I step into the *Breath of Hell* – thick with heat and the smell of rotting faeces, the air dead. The earth a baked grey-white. I wade through to the other side. Climb the steps toward my old cell and walk in.

No one moves. Their heads are down, listening to radios turned up full blast. An incomprehensible rant. I pick up the words 'Democratic Republic of Afghanistan' spoken at high speed. Deafening.

I see Sediqua but stay where I am, standing at the entrance, the very same place I hesitated on my first night here.

Thank goodness. She's turning the radio down. Its sound had been ricocheting off the walls.

She is looking up. 'Afghanistan – *democracy*, like you, like Western country,' she exclaims, wide-eyed and excited. This is what the broadcaster has decreed and they believe it.

'No, Sediqua, not democracy, just name. No freedom for Afghan people, the government is communist Russia.' I'm in no mood to allow a lie to deceive these already deceived, betrayed women.

Sediqua looks at me oddly. Does she not understand what I am saying? Or not want to hear what I am saying?

She rejects my statement with a look of defiance and turns away. I understand. She has to have hope, no matter how impossible. And I have no right to intrude.

'Amnesty for prisoners. Government give amnesty for prisoners,' she finally retorts, emphatically.

'Yes. Good,' I smile.

She sighs.

I have to admit the prison does feel emptier than during my previous incarceration. Something has changed, and although it's too soon for me to know whether it is less populated, the atmosphere emanates a prickly edginess. Its former insularity and community is somehow fractured. Is it because the women are anticipating their release? Is it this summer heat?

Or has it something to do with that long red banner draped across that concrete wall within my eye's view from our cell? On the banner is a white-chalked, superhuman image of a crouching woman shackled in chains. Huge white tears dot down the red cloth into an oceanic wave of words.

Is this the prisoners' plea for mercy? And who is it meant to be seen by? It's not visible from outside the prison compound.

As a symbol it is extremely forlorn.

My 'one night' passes in a sleep induced by mild suffocation rather than natural causes. The cell was a hot airless tomb, the day's windless heat trapped by the walls. All but the older mother slept in the fetid air out in the courtyard, or along the concrete veranda. I guess this is their system of survival during the summer.

Time dawdles along, dragging toward afternoon.

2pm. I can see the policewoman and clerk preparing to lock up their office. What about me?

They are oblivious. That judge has deliberately deceived me. I won't be released today. I feel *murder* rising in my heart toward her – that *bitch* who put me in here.

Slowly, I realise the impotence of my anger. Sadness takes its place.

But why? Why this lie that seeks to steal another's life?

## fifty-two

A second night has passed. The morning has passed, it spent half-pie occupied in watching little Muhammad and his mates torturing a large moth. They had tied a long white cotton thread to it, and no matter how hard the moth beat the air – and like a kite they let it rise and try to fly – the little creature would eventually die of exhaustion.

It is now the dead heat of mid-afternoon.

No *Vic-to-ria* call to the visitors' grate, as had been the routine during my last imprisonment. A woman prisoner, one I don't recognise, comes up to me. 'Visitor.'

It is Jens, well dressed, clean-shaven and clear-eyed, bending to peer at me through the iron bars.

'Poor little Victoria, this is too *much*, too *much*.' Shaking his head.

I can find nothing to say, just look into his eyes. They are the same blue eyes I met when I was apprehended at Kabul airport, when he too was a prisoner, all those lifetimes ago.

'Can I do anything for you, Victoria?' It is a useless question but that is not the point. He casts a final backward glance as he leaves…

A grunt from behind me. Queen Candi is wearing the same corner-throne persona I recall from last time: that of a stern, unapproachable authority.
What's this? She is handing me a brown paper bag. A *camera*! A beaten-up 35mm Pentax. I recognise it – it is the one I had borrowed from the Danish tourist to photograph the tank. And *three* rolls of film. I glance back at the Queen. She is aware of what the bag contains. Is pleased for me.

Evening of my second day. Something is amiss; a sick woman has been brought into our cell. *Very* sick. I don't know why they have brought her in here, but judging by the concerned expressions of Sediqua and other women tending her, her illness is dangerous. Her face is blackish, and she's unconscious. Is it contagious?

'Doctor come, doctor come,' Sediqua says when she sees me looking. She is frightened.

The doctor is a Western-dressed, bearded Afghan about Assilan's age. He looks at her, is concerned. He sits by her body and picks up her arm to take the woman's pulse. Is putting his stethoscope into his ears, listening to her heartbeat.

He peels back her eyelids. Beads of perspiration run down his face. He looks around, singles out and speaks hurriedly to Sediqua, who is all attention. She dashes out of the cell. He talks to the other women.

A group of soldiers enter carrying a stretcher and the women help the doctor to roll their ill sister onto it. They look as if they are touching something deadly.

The soldiers carry her out.

The doctor notices me sitting in the far corner and I stare mutely back. He looks concerned. Has gone.

Sediqua, in a fluster of worry and activity, rushes back into this cell, her hands waving frantically, her eyes wide and glistening. 'Cholera! Cholera!' she is almost shouting.

*Mother of Mercy…*

Night. I am not going to sleep where that woman lay. Am I going to sleep at all? Pillowless, breathing the same air that woman must have exhaled. Did she exhale? If she didn't maybe I am safe?

So hot, so sticky *hot*. Perhaps I have a fever? Or is it just that my cotton clothes are soaked with two days of perspiration?

I realise that I've never seen the women change their clothes, undress. I have seen clothes strung out along the courtyard – colours flying, drying. But I've never seen them get changed.

*I will not die.*

It's morning, and I haven't caught cholera – don't feel any more unwell than usual. A small relief, but a relief nonetheless.

I walk out onto the stone veranda and sit on an unoccupied hemp-rope bed. It's hot and stinks but is shaded. Several other beds are spread about the courtyard, some of them occupied. Are they ill? Babies and children crawl about.

The afternoon heat drives me back inside the cell.

A woman is poking her head around the corner of the cell's entrance, gesturing to me to go to the visitors' room…

I cannot hug him through the iron door; I hug him with my eyes.

He'd gone to my room and, when I'd not been there as arranged, realised what had happened. He tells me the servant boy is an informer and that the woman judge has left Kabul. That she won't release me.

Assilan shifts his body and looks at me squarely. 'There is no more law in Afghanistan. The soldiers are executing people at random. Your situation is now very dangerous. As I know you have no more money I will use my own to hire a lawyer and try to have you cleared. This is the only way you will be released.'

Spies and enemies, death and war: how real yet foreign it all is to my Pacific person. And all I can do is look into Assilan's eyes, folding… with

*ineffable tenderness,*

Closing me in them…

He silently backs away.

Uplifted by Assilan's visit I recognise my opportunity. I have a camera, three rolls of film and an unsuppressable urge to portray the women…

They are willing, open. They want to be remembered – engage with me and the world I represent.

I now have a record of Afghanistan's imprisoned women and children – the forgotten faces, *not* the Police Minister's promise of forbidden places. What an irony.

Night – I am dreaming. My mother is looking for me; has found me; wants to rescue me. I'm resuscitated by seeing her, yet disturbed. I do not want her to risk her life to save me.

It is the only dream I have had in all this time. And awakens me – returns me to my cultural and self-identity; who I was, am.

Day four, or five? Mid-morning.

Assilan is back. He has found a lawyer. My case is to be heard the following morning.

I'm terribly nervous, stomach-delicate.

Night. A blowfly. It has hunted me down as I try to sleep, is

*buzzzzzzzzzzzzing*

around me. Its persistence feels as ominous as that of those metal-jets-of-death screaming out of the sky at the height of the war.

I can't sleep; it's too hot. Dozing… buzzzzzzzzzz, the fly waking me again. Finally I drift off…

– What?

Who is *shaking* me? Breaking into my much-needed rest?

A shape in the darkness. Queen Candi. Sitting close to my head.

I want to sleep…

She's shaking me again. *Annoying* me. I look up at her, vibe her to *leave me alone*. I can vaguely see her face. Why is she here? Is she deliberately keeping me from sleep? Does she know I'm to face the judges in the morning and want me to look even more haggard when I stand before them? I figure yes.

Struggling to stay awake, staring up toward the Queen's face. She is motionless, is watching over me, protectively.

Finally I relax in her presence, sensing her fighter's soul. Scarred. Loyal.

I can't hear her breathe. There's so little air in here.

## fifty-three

The Queen shakes me awake again and the sun is up. She must have let me sleep in the end but it wasn't enough. I am tired, *nervous*, biliously nervous. I stalk across the stinking courtyard to the stinking hellhole.

An old woman holding a bucket and a twig broom greets me as I enter. She is engaged in a losing battle, swishing the overflowing sewage back toward its intended repositories, slopping buckets of water into the mess.

I wade through the yellow ooze. It soaks between my toes – *squelching*, adding to a temper equally foul.

Some teenage girls come in to ogle at me. Their intruding eyes serve to fuel my *anger*…

At 9am the soldiers take me to the courtroom. As I walk toward the building I see Assilan waiting outside, talking to a man in a Western suit. He – the lawyer – requests that I sign a document written in Persian.

'What does this say?' I'm concerned. On guard.

'It's our only chance. It says you are innocent because you didn't know it was illegal to take hashish out of the country. You *must* sign it.'

Assilan is saying this to me, with urgency.

What if it's not accepted? I decide there and then that if this hearing is unsuccessful I'm going to climb through the hole in the prison that Marie's son uses to spy on the world. I've discovered it. If need be I will enlist the gargoyle's help thereafter.

Assilan has a pen at the ready. I trust him. I know that just by being here with me he is risking his life. I cannot expect anything more from him if this plea is denied.

I have signed.

We enter the courtroom.

They are the same judges, the same tea-party patriarchs who'd pardoned me on the morning of the revolution. They look fragile. Are they too under threat?

They read and discuss the lawyer's plea. Are deliberating.

Finally ready to give their verdict.

They conclude inconclusively: I am to be released from prison immediately. There is to be no monetary fine, but they are to confiscate my cameras.

I realised long ago that they would not be returned to me, that their cash value was too great.

Outside the courtroom Assilan explains to me that I have to go back to the prison and wait for my release papers, which will take no longer than about ten minutes. He will wait for me outside the prison door.

I had underestimated her power; that seemingly inconsequential policewoman stooping over her desk in her office close to the hellhole. It is her signature that I now need.

'Half an hour, then finished,' she says bluntly. The clerk sitting next to her has a blind eye. I haven't seen it up close before. He looks at me balefully with his one good eye.

Half an hour. I hadn't reckoned on this, nor this blockade of blues, greens, purples, whites, oranges, reds and bits of arms, bodies merging, crowding around the visitors' room. It must be Saturday. It's impossible to reach Assilan to tell him of this small delay.

Shrieking, babbling; so *loud*, frenetic.

'Please *hurry up*, policewoman in your office, and sign my release,' I gasp out loud.

Another half an hour.

So *hot*.

'Soon.' She's not even lifting her eyes. Why is she doing this – is it to hold me victim to her petty power?

Two hours pass. My eyes ache. The sun's heat shimmers, bouncing off the walls, frying, melting me down.

But I'm not – going – to – shift – from her sight. I am not going to let her close her office and pretend I don't exist.

I'm staring at her from over here, on the concrete parapet; willing her to *give me my release papers*.

The prisoners swirl around, their colours merging; a mirage. Waves of heat. It must be forty-five degrees. Their shrieking, shrieking. So brittle.

So *tired*…

The clerk is lifting his head, is looking over at me, nodding his head. The papers, my release…

A *shout,* loud sharp. It issued from inside the visitors' room just a few yards to my left.

What's happening? The women are reeling, their cacophony hushed. Rushing frantically across the courtyard into their cells… Queen Candi is herding them. Her knuckles are white, tight-gripped around her whip. Fear creases her face.

They have all vanished.

A hush.

The courtyard is whisperless, empty except for me…

The large gate next to the prisoners' viewing room is opening. A commandant and one, two, three, four, five, six soldiers are marching in, along the parapet. Halting no more than twenty feet away from me. The commandant is dressed in an impeccable gold, red and white uniform.

The soldiers present arms. The commandant turns his head and sees me. Is staring at me.

*Dumbstruck*. The soldier second from his right is lifting his rifle, is *aiming* it at my heart!

A loud call, coming from inside one of the cells. I'm not moving a muscle but my peripheral vision catches a shape – *Queen Candi*, hurrying-running-hurrying. Her arms are raised like scythes cutting the air as she waves frantically at the commandant.

She's calling, talking loudly at him as she hurries toward him. How small and *vulnerable* she suddenly looks.

She stops a short distance below him. The commandant looks arrogantly down at her as her words fly, her hands gesture wildly. She is stabbing her forefinger toward me – to her ear, twirling it around and around, indicating that I'm crazy? Saying: 'Hashish, hashish!'

She's pleading for my life.

The commandant looks at me. Is appraising me. I can read his face: I'm of no consequence.

He gestures to his soldier, who lowers his gun.

Queen Candi bows to the commandant, an infinitely subtle feminine bow. Turns her back to him and with svelte, feline grace hurries back to her cell. A nervous involuntary smile flickering across her lips as she does so.

That brave woman has just saved my life.

The commandant reassumes his erect stature, stares straight ahead. His soldiers stiffen to attention.

I am as immobile as the almond trees. Watching.

A soldier enters through the open gate, followed by a most frail and dignified old woman in a tailored suit. She must be in her eighties. Her steps are uncertain. Her eyes, focused on the ground, are ringed with deep brown shadows and grief; weighted with enormous sorrow. She slowly follows the soldier through to the walkway leading to the well and the top-security wing.

A moment later two more women are led in – teenagers, wearing fashionably faded jeans. They walk quickly; their eyes also dark-ringed with grief, also focused on the ground.

Now a noble, defiant-looking boy of about twelve is led in by another soldier. His eyes are also to the ground but he lifts them momentarily, quick-glancing around the prison courtyard. The soldiers didn't see.

Two prepubescent girls with beautiful young faces and a mien beyond their years move like gazelles.

A young woman of about twenty with finely chiselled features and an ascetic beauty walks in alone. She passes a few feet to my left. Her heart is broken.

An ethereal silence permeates the prison.

A soldier is coming through the gate, his rifle slung across his back. A few feet behind him a very small boy, aged about three, with a child's open, innocent face. He has the bearing, the upright proud posture of a little king.

Another soldier follows the child, whose little toddler legs are hurrying to keep up with the man in front. I can see that he is struggling with all his child's might to keep his eyes lowered, his troubled expression betraying his confusion.

As the child disappears the commandant and his men march out and the women tumble out into the courtyard.

'Royal family of Afghanistan – president's cousin brother family, *royal family…*' Sediqua pauses to tell me breathlessly before slipping back into her native tongue.

It feels so awfully wrong; such authentic dignity being subjected to such brutality and degradation. I feel ill.

Get away out of here is all I can think as I sidle my way through the throng of excited women toward the policewoman's office. I thrust out my arm in silent demand. My release papers are handed over. I grab the brown paper bag from my cell.

The prison door is opened for me.

I'm quick to step beyond it.

Once outside I am hit by waves of shock and grief. I know that those fine-looking people, a lineage, are to die. Not even the child will be spared.

I can't see Assilan anywhere. The whole of the prison compound is deserted.

A taxi back to the hotel.

Peeling off my fetid clothes.

In my absence the servant boy, the informer, the gargoyle tells me, has 'gone'.

## fifty-four

Assilan appears the following morning. He tells me that the signature of release from the presiding Supreme Court judge is required before I can repossess my passport.

I had thought I was free…

We taxi back out to the Supreme Court Chambers, and hurry up the steps into a portico lined with Corinthian columns.

Now we are passing through the door we'd seen the socialist leader escorted through a day before the 'revolution'.

We enter the Supreme Court judges' chamber. A Supreme Court judge is within. Assilan momentarily freezes on seeing him, then he approaches and speaks to him. I have no comprehension of what is being discussed. I can only read the judge's face: the same thin tight lips I have seen so often on the faces of people holding high office in this country: hooked nose, vulturish. *Mean.*

His decision: I must await Supreme Court trial. Maybe a year, maybe never.

He wants me to die, wants me dead.

Retreating back down the stairs, Assilan is close to tears. Suddenly he stops and turns back, saying to me, 'Wait, wait.'

I carry on down, out into the portico. Prowling between the pillars. A force wells up – not tears, not disappointment, not grief, not anger.

*Rage.*

*Accursed land.*

I shall escape. Through the Khyber Pass – not by the asphalt road I travelled up months earlier; there is an older road used since time immemorial by tribesmen, gypsies, merchants, conquerors, and their armies.

I picture myself in a grey-brown burka, fleeing from this insane land; moving silently, swiftly along riverbeds, mountain tracks. I'm *invisible;* subsumed in the Absolute, the Earth. *Fleeing.*

Footsteps behind me.

Assilan. 'Come, I have seen the Minister and told him your mother is very sick and he must let you go.'

Remounting the stairs. Entering the office of the 'new' Minister of Justice for Afghanistan. Following Assilan's instructions, I say to this man, who does not lift his face to look at me: 'Please let me free this day, as my mother is very ill.'

I don't care what he decides to decide about my life. All that matters is that *I am going to run away, run away, run away, run.*

'Kilosh.' Finished.

He's agreed.

I've hardly registered.

There are three days until my air ticket expires. I have a few US dollars left, and Assilan has retrieved my passport.

I book my ticket out – the only available flight is on the last valid day. I'm nearly *Out Out Out. Out!*

To celebrate my reclaimed liberty Assilan suggests I go with him and one of his landowning student friends 'to a place where you shall have 360-degree views'. I *hunger* for a vista. Elevation.

It's an hour's drive by slow taxi from the outskirts of Kabul. On the way we pass a battalion of soldiers, but they are unconcerned with outgoing traffic.

We stop at the base of a large barren hill. Assilan's friend Nouri leads as we climb a path that weaves its way up. Halfway up Nouri meets the region's tribal chieftain. Overjoyed to see his feudal landowner-master the chieftain skip-dances with open arms and a huge smile toward him, embracing him like a beloved brother. He leads Nouri off toward his village.

Assilan and I keep climbing. Climbing. To the top of the hill.

I have not *breathed* thin, clear summer air nor seen the Earth's sweeping infinitudes for a very long time. What *bliss* for my mountain, forest, nature-loving soul to look around… and *down*… to see the city in its true perspective: no more than a distant grubby blot on a landscape otherwise majestically wild and untameable.

I look for the prison. Too far away. Non-existent.

We share the mood; nature's *elevating* vastness. Our aloneness.

Slowly descending, we find Nouri and return to the waiting taxi and its edgy, chain-smoking driver. The soldiers have unnerved him. Before we'd set out on our climb he had wanted to be paid, then no doubt would have dashed back without us. It was my presence that scared him. Assilan had convinced him that going back without us would be even more dangerous.

I sit next to Assilan in the back seat, behind the driver.

We are within a few hundred yards of them. They are spreading out onto the road. Are waving us down. There is no way past.

'Look straight ahead and do not answer any questions. I will say that you are from the peace corps,' Assilan whispers as we slow to a stop.

The soldiers crowd around the taxi. Assilan unwinds the window and speaks to them, then turns to me. 'They want to see your passport.'

I've been hugging it to my body from the moment it was returned to me. With my eyes lowered I pass it to Assilan, who gives it to the soldiers.

They flick through it, look up at me, flick through it again. Are staring through the window at me. I can see them through the corners of my eyes.

*Keep staring straight in front of you. Do not meet their eyes. Keep staring straight in front of you.*

I can hear Assilan saying 'peace corps'.

In unison the soldiers counter with 'white imperialist spy'.

I can feel them; they are looking intently at me, their forms shadows against the light... *Do not feel their breath hitting you as they poke their heads through the window. Look calm. Professional.*

'Peace corps,' Assilan reiterates, calmly.

Something hits me.

My passport; they have flung it at my lap. Assilan winds up the window. The driver drives on.

We sit in silence for the rest of the journey.

## fifty-five

*They shaved his head
to clothe him in ugliness
out of jealousy and fear of his beauty,
they erased the night
and left him in dawn.*
             Yusuf ibn Harun al-Ramadi, 1022

I spend my last morning in Afghanistan finding out the procedure for recovering my films. In all this business no one has mentioned that they are to be confiscated.

I have now been through almost every ground-floor office in the maze that is the judicial zone of the prison compound, and I am now being finger-pointed toward a door in a building fifty feet away where the right authority, the chief of police, resides.

I open a door to a narrow waiting room with two long benches facing each other. At the end of the room sits a sullen clerk behind his desk, closed doors on either side of him. The clerk motions me to wait. I am prepared to wait; there are two and a half hours before the offices close.

Half an hour. An hour. I approach the sullen clerk. Another lazy gesture indicating to me to wait.

Three-quarters of an hour remain before the offices close. I am now *agitated*.

The door to the clerk's left is opening… a prisoner and two jailers are coming in. My eyes follow the prisoner: naked but for a long ragged brown tunic tied at his shoulder; two lengths of chain, each length grasped by a soldier, connect to a metal collar around his neck, holding him in total submission. His wrists are shackled in irons.

With a clinking sound they move toward and sit on the bench opposite me.

The prisoner's ankles are also shackled. Over time the leg irons have bitten deeply into the flesh, which is raw, ridged with scars and weeping scabs. His feet are large, splay-toed, dust covered. The soldiers' boots are worn, broken and untied, their coarse uniforms stained and wet.

An acrid smell whiffs into my nostrils: stale urine. Men's.

The soldiers' faces are Big, Bristled, Burly.

*Brutes.* Of the raw-flesh-eating variety.

My eyes slide half-focused over the face in the middle, not wanting to meet his. The prisoner's eyes are down. I scan him: shaven, handsome. Lighter boned than the chunk-jawed brutes holding him; a tall forehead, pronounced cheekbones, long sinewy arms. And a skull that falls away dramatically at the back of his head – as if a knife had sliced it in half. He is the 'madman' whose desolate cries had broken the prison's night. The 'Neanderthal'.

I glance over to the clerk hoping to catch his eye. His head is also down; he hasn't bothered to look up to see who has entered the room.

Silence. The 'madman', head bowed toward his chest, is as silent as the wall behind him. The clerk is bent toward his desk. The soldiers' grey eyes are vacant.

Time is pressing heavily. I am staring vaguely across at the three figures on the opposite bench, my mind fixed on the clerk to my left, willing *it* to attend to me.

The madman is lifting his face. Is throwing back his head, eyes to the ceiling.

'Ha!' the madman laughs. A short single laugh.

The two soldiers are bending their heads across the prisoner's chest, are sniggering to each other; brute mirroring brute across the heart of their captive.

I am the clerk's captive. He holds the key to time, my time. Or thinks he does. I stand, again approach him. 'Chief police,' I demand, staring forcefully down at his black Brylcreem-glued head. It doesn't budge. He is point-blank refusing to acknowledge my existence.

My patience bursts. I turn from the clerk and stride over to the door.

Holding onto the handle, I look in, see his head bent over his desk. He has someone with him. *Quickly*, pull back, shut the door. Heart pounding. Oh what a dangerous, stupid thing I almost did. *He* is in there. The beast: the Minister of Police.

Something in me snaps. I'm shouting, shouting at the unhearing immovable clerk, shouting, shouting, incomprehensibly... *ranting...* Breaking down.

I slump backward onto the bench and sink my head upon my chest, as silent as the wall behind me. Weeping.

And for eternity may so have remained. But something – an intensity not my own – compels me to look up. Into the eyes of the madman. He is also weeping, his eyes filled with tears...

*Supreme innocence...*

Stilled by the madman, I rise and leave that narrow room.

Without my films.

Back in the hotel I cut off my hair.

That night Assilan – Buddha man, lion man – comes to me.
    Such a love it is,
    two hearts beating as the other
    Flesh liquid, immortal,
    One.

The following morning we are at the airport.
    Last night lovers, saying goodbye.
    His last words to me: 'I promised you that I would see you free.'

# Epilogue

I heard from Assilan some months later. Enclosed in his letter were a number of my films. He'd managed to buy some of them back and had apparently paid for this 'blackmail' with a month in prison.

He told me that between ten and twelve thousand people were being 'disappeared' each month; that killing and mass incarceration began in earnest within a month of my departure.

By the end of 1979, other than noting that Afghanistan was caught in a bloody and deepening war, I turned away. I had my own post-trauma experiences to cope with: terror at the slightest sound; frequent nightmares of explosions and thwarted escapes, fires and haunting faces.

It wasn't until 1992 that Afghanistan again resurfaced in my thoughts when I started to write the story and it took me to New York.

Here, and one day I found myself ascending the steps from the subway to Times Square. Wads of chewing gum, flattened and stained black from the grime of passing feet, complemented the stale air. I reached the street and looked around.

I knew this city, Manhattan: I'd lived here during the late 1980s. I decided to walk east, toward Fifth Avenue, then changed my mind. No, I didn't want to go back into the familiarity of this city. My present journey was older; it was a memory journey back in time, back to Afghanistan. But, why New York?

*Turn around. Don't think*, memory seemed to say, and I found myself in a street I hadn't been in before. My attention was caught by a book in a shop window. *Art in Afghanistan*. I bought it. It was the first visual contact I'd had with anything Afghan for fourteen years. I walked along the street flicking through the pages.

Glancing in another shop window, I saw a vase strikingly similar to one I'd just been looking at in my new book. Amazed, I walked into the shop. The shopkeeper was an Afghan and the vase was indeed the very same one.

On impulse I asked the shopkeeper if by chance he had heard of my friend Assilan. Miraculously, he had.

'The family and the doctor you name fled Afghanistan and are living somewhere in California.' I couldn't believe my ears.

The telephone operator couldn't find the name. California is, after all, a very large state. Eventually I gave up. A couple of weeks passed. Then there was another nudge. The cousin of a friend wanted someone to mind her house in Berkeley, California, while she went on holiday. I volunteered.

In Berkeley my yearning to find Assilan grew. He was there, here, somewhere. I searched out every Afghan restaurant and antique shop I could find. Nothing: no one had heard of the name. It was an impossible chance. I decided to give up.

*Turn around. Don't think.* There was that voice again. Again I obeyed. I followed my feet.

They led me into a rundown shopping mall, to the very back of it. Here, out of sight, was a small Afghan restaurant. Half-heartedly I asked the youth behind the counter if he knew the name Assilan. Of course he didn't. Feeling ridiculous, I had just turned to walk away when an older woman came out from the restaurant's kitchen and called to me.

Could I please repeat my question? I did. And yes, she knew the name, she knew the man. He had married her best friend and was living in Queens, New York. She had his telephone number.

His voice was the same.

We arranged to meet at 4pm outside my apartment in New York. I stood in the cold, Manhattan's endless traffic rushing by. I looked up and down the street, up and down. At twenty past four I began to wonder if I'd given him the wrong address, or if he'd lost it. Perhaps he didn't want to meet me.

Then I looked across the road and saw him. He was wearing sunglasses, had a moustache, and was dressed in an ill-fitting black suit. His smile was the same. We drove down to the Cornelius Street cafe.

Assilan removed his sunglasses and reached for his cigarettes; he had become a chain-smoker. His eyes were unchanged: they hadn't lost their depth, their Buddha-like calm as he recounted what had happened to him since our parting.

He had gone to Pakistan to work in a refugee camp. There he had to cut through the gangrenous, shrapnel-embedded, torn muscles and shattered bones of eight to ten women and children a day, often without anaesthetic. Two years of this and he said he almost went insane.

He fled to the US, where he had to sit all his medical exams again. Now he was working thirty-six-hour shifts to feed his extended family of 200. He wanted to help his country and people. There was no international aid to support its recovery.

We talked for five hours – talked ourselves into fatigue and beyond. I began to feel very, very tired. It had something to do with reconnecting with the past, I'm sure of that.

'We are just flesh and blood,' I remember saying to him after his descriptions of the wounded and dead and dying. 'And bone,' he had replied, with finality.

the plates

# images of Pakistan and Afghanistan

## 1978

# section one

# a portrait of the author's journey

Author's note: The images represent a part only of the study,
a number of films were not recovered.

PAKISTAN
Lahore

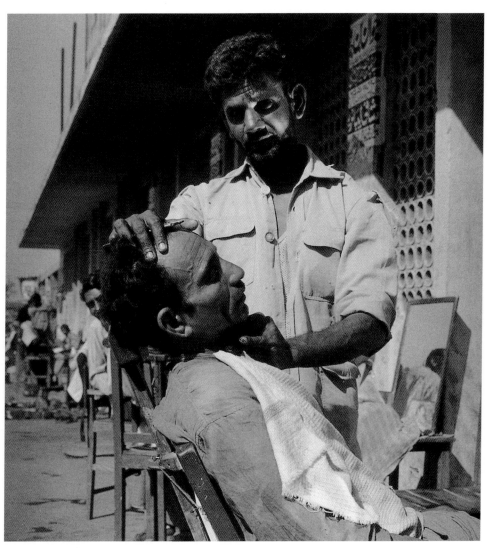

PLATE TWO

PLATE THREE

PLATE FOUR

PLATE FIVE

PLATE SIX

PLATE SEVEN

PLATE EIGHT

PLATE NINE

PLATE TEN

PLATE ELEVEN

PLATE TWELVE

PLATE THIRTEEN

PLATE FOURTEEN

PLATE FIFTEEN

PLATE SIXTEEN

PLATE SEVENTEEN

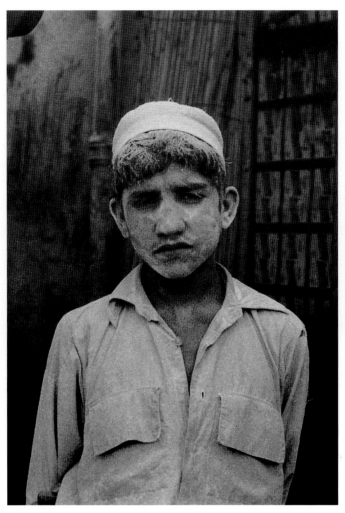

PLATE EIGHTEEN

PLATE NINETEEN

PLATE TWENTY

PLATE TWENTY-ONE

PLATE TWENTY-TWO

PLATE TWENTY-THREE

PLATE TWENTY-FOUR

PLATE TWENTY-FIVE

PLATE TWENTY-SIX

PLATE TWENTY-SEVEN

PLATE TWENTY-EIGHT

PLATE TWENTY-NINE

PLATE THIRTY

PLATE THIRTY-ONE

PLATE THIRTY-TWO

PLATE THIRTY-THREE

PLATE THIRTY-FOUR

PLATE THIRTY-FIVE

PLATE THIRTY-SIX

PLATE THIRTY-SEVEN

# section two
# Kabul Women's Prison

A portrait of the prisoners.

Sediqua.

View across the mud courtyard from my cell.

View across the mud courtyard of my cell. Behind the two women.

A soldier patrolling on the roof above my cell.

Soldiers removing rubbish. Queen Candi to the right, back view.

PLATE FORTY-THREE

PLATE FORTY-FOUR

PLATE FORTY-FIVE

PLATE FORTY-SIX

The prison gate, visitors viewing room, and walkway through to the well.

The 'pock-marked girl' from my cell – a 'prison maid' – and boy.

The other 'prison maid' from my cell.

PLATE FIFTY

PLATE FIFTY-ONE

PLATE FIFTY-TWO

PLATE FIFTY-THREE

PLATE FIFTY-FOUR

Little Muhammed.

PLATE FIFTY-SIX

PLATE FIFTY-SEVEN

PLATE FIFTY-EIGHT

The 'older mother' in our cell.

PLATE SIXTY

PLATE SIXTY-ONE

PLATE SIXTY-TWO

PLATE SIXTY-THREE

A 'beauty' posing on the steps to the 'hell-hole'.

In the late afternoon shade. Sediqua dancing.

PLATE SIXTY-SIX

The 'plump young madonna' from my cell.

PLATE SIXTY-SEVEN

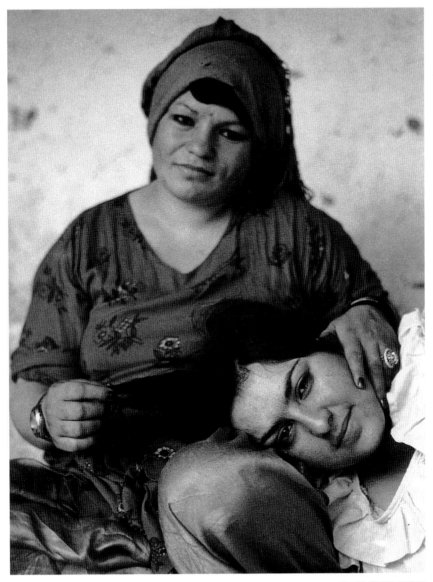

Queen Candi and Marie.